Fireworks

Vampires, Elephants and Aliens

ANTHOLOGY

Gill & Macmillan
Hume Avenue
Park West
Dublin 12
www.gillmacmillan.ie

ISBN: 9780717153169
© John Hartnett, Eithne Kennedy, Patricia O'Doherty, Eileen Phelan 2012

Design: Aisli Madden / Outburst Design
Cover illustration: Aisli Madden
Inside illustrations: MSM Studios, Brian Fitzgerald,
Úna Woods, ODI Illustrators.
Printed by Edelvives, Spain

First published March 2012

The paper used in this book is made from the wood pulp of managed forests. For every tree felled, at least one tree is planted, thereby renewing natural resources.

Dear Reader,

Welcome to *Vampires, Elephants and Aliens*. This anthology is filled with a wide range of interesting fiction, poetry and non-fiction pieces. We hope you have as much fun reading this selection, as we had in putting it together.

The fiction includes extracts from lots of different kinds of stories: funny ones, sad ones, historical stories, fantasies, mysteries, as well as graphic novels and classics. We hope that if you really like an author or a story you will go on to read the entire novel and find other titles in that genre or by the same author.

Within the non-fiction, there is a variety of pieces, from information to interviews to puzzles. You can read about topics that link up with some of the fiction themes. For example, after an historical fiction story there may be a factual piece that shows you what life was really like during that period. Then there are pieces relating to the kinds of reading you may have to do in order to locate information or to complete a task e.g. how to read a timetable or a recipe. These pieces have lots of photographs, tables, maps and headings to help you learn about the topic.

As well as introducing you to a range of genres, this book is designed to help you boost your reading skills and develop the strategies that good readers use. There are 'before reading', 'during reading' and 'after reading' questions or prompts to help you along the way. Let's take a look at some of these special features.

Before reading:

Think of this as a warm-up activity for reading. It is about getting your mind ready to read the text. We may ask you to make predictions about what you imagine the text

1. Read the title of the extract and look at the illustrations. What do you think the story will be about? Make a prediction.
2. How often are the Olympic Games held?
3. Where were the most recent Olympic Games held? Where will the next ones be held?

Olympic Marathon

Morris Gleitzman

will be about by checking the title, examining the artwork or photographs, scanning and reading headings, or considering what you already know about the topic or the author's style of writing.

During reading:

Notice the little stars on the page. These are a signal to you to check out the prompt or question in the coloured box at the end of the page before you read on. It is also a signal to slow down your reading and to ponder this important element of the story. We might ask you to notice how the author creates a mood or how a character is feeling or why they reacted to a particular event in the story.

All except me.
I just sat there and watched Dad try to do a delighted cartwheel and crash into the electric bug zapper.
'Here we go,' I muttered to Hoppy. 'We're cactus, now.'
It started that evening.

Why do you think the boy doesn't want the games to be held in Australia?

8

After reading (fiction):

Notice the icons on the left-hand side. They are a signal to you that you have to think differently in order to answer the question.

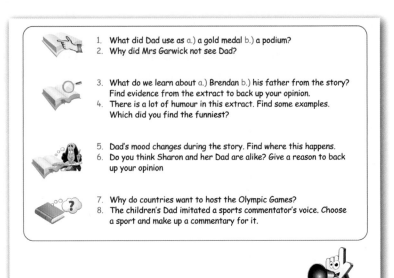

1. What did Dad use as a.) a gold medal b.) a podium?
2. Why did Mrs Garwick not see Dad?

3. What do we learn about a.) Brendan b.) his father from the story? Find evidence from the extract to back up your opinion.
4. There is a lot of humour in this extract. Find some examples. Which did you find the funniest?

5. Dad's mood changes during the story. Find where this happens.
6. Do you think Sharon and her Dad are alike? Give a reason to back up your opinion

7. Why do countries want to host the Olympic Games?
8. The children's Dad imitated a sports commentator's voice. Choose a sport and make up a commentary for it.

 These questions ask you to recall details from the story. There is only one right answer and you can find it in one particular spot in the story.

 These questions also ask you to recall some details from the story. The answer is in the text but you will have to find it in different parts of the story and put it all together to respond correctly. This section may also draw attention to particular words or phrases in the story.

 These questions ask you to read between the lines. This means the question cannot be answered directly from the text and there is no one right answer. These questions are great 'conversation starters'. You may also find your answer or opinion differs to that of your classmates. You will need to back up your answer with evidence from the text, so you may have to re-read parts of the story and think deeply about these questions.

 These questions also relate to the story but go beyond it. The answer is not in the text. In fact, you could answer the question without having read the text. They are 'real world' questions that may ask you to think about the theme of the story or a particular topic or issue. These too are great 'conversation starters'.

At the end of each extract, we have (where possible) included the cover of the book it was taken from and earmarked if an audio recording of this extract is available on our website: www.fireworksenglish.ie

So happy reading, thinking and debating... go have some fun; lose yourself in a story, a poem or discover something new in an information piece.

Contents

Danny the Champion of the World

Roald Dahl

Chapter two: The Big Friendly Giant

My father without the slightest doubt, was the most marvellous and exciting father any boy ever had. Here is a picture of him.

You might think, if you didn't know him well, that he was a stern and serious man. He wasn't. He was actually a wildly funny person. What made him appear so serious was the fact that he never smiled with his mouth. He did it all with his eyes. He had brilliant blue eyes and when he thought of something funny, his eyes would flash and if you looked carefully, you could actually see a tiny little golden spark dancing in the middle of each eye. But the mouth never moved.

I was glad my father was an eye-smiler. It meant he never gave me a fake smile because it's impossible to make your eyes twinkly if you aren't feeling twinkly yourself. A mouth-smile is different. You can fake a mouth-smile any time you want, simply by moving your lips. I've also learned that a real mouth-smile always has an eye-smile to go with it, so watch out, I say, when someone smiles at you with his mouth but the eyes stay the same. It's sure to be bogus.

My father was not what you would call an educated man and I doubt if he had read 20 books in his life. But he was a marvellous story-teller. He used to make up a bedtime story for me every single night, and the best ones were turned into serials and went on for many nights running.

One of them, which must have gone on for at least fifty nights, was about an enormous fellow called The Big Friendly Giant, or The BFG for short. The BFG was three times as tall as an ordinary man and his hands were as big as wheelbarrows. He lived in a vast underground cavern not far from our filling station and he only came out into the open when it was dark. Inside the cavern he had a powder-factory where he made more than a hundred different kinds of magic powder.

Occasionally, as he told his stories, my father would stride up and down waving his arms and waggling his fingers. But mostly he would sit close to me on the edge of my bunk and speak very softly.

'The Big Friendly Giant makes his magic powders out of the dreams that children dream when they are asleep,' he said.

'How?' I asked. 'Tell me how, Dad.'

'Dreams, my love, are very mysterious things. They float around in the night air like little clouds, searching for sleeping people.'

'Can you see them?' I asked.

'Nobody can see them.'

'Then how does The Big Friendly Giant catch them?'

'Ah,' my father said. 'That is the interesting part. A dream, you see, as it goes drifting through the night air, makes a tiny little buzzing-humming sound, a sound so soft and low it is impossible for ordinary people to hear it. But the BFG can hear it easily. His sense of hearing is absolutely fantastic.'

I loved the far intent look on my father's face when he was telling a story. His face was pale and still and distant, unconscious of everything around him.

'The BFG,' he said, 'can hear the tread of a ladybird's footsteps as she walks across a leaf. He can hear the whisperings of ants as they scurry around in the soil talking to one another. He can hear the sudden shrill cry of pain a tree gives out when a woodman cuts into it with an axe. Ah yes, my darling, there is a whole world of sound around us that we cannot hear because our ears are simply not sensitive enough.'

What have you learned about Danny's father so far?

2

'What happens when he catches the dreams?' I asked.

'He imprisons them in glass bottles and screws the tops down tight,' my father said. 'He has thousands of these bottles in his cave.'

'Does he catch bad dreams as well as good ones?'

'Yes,' my father said. 'He catches both. But he only uses the good ones in his powders.'

'What does he do with the bad ones?'

'He explodes them.'

It is impossible to tell you how much I loved my father.

When he was sitting close to me on my bunk I would reach out and slide my hand into his, and then he would fold his long fingers around my fist, holding it tight.

'What does The BFG do with his powders after he has made them?' I asked.

'In the dead of night,' my father said, 'he goes prowling through the villages searching for houses where children are asleep. Because of his great height he can reach windows that are one and even two flights up, and when he finds a room with a sleeping child, he opens his suitcase...'

'His suitcase?' I said.

'The BFG always carries a suitcase and a blowpipe,' my father said. 'The blowpipe is as long as a lamp-post. The suitcase is for the powders. So he opens the suitcase and selects exactly the right powder... and he puts it into the blowpipe... and he slides the blowpipe in through the open window... and *poof*... he blows in the powder... and the powder floats around the room... and the child breathes it in...'

'And then what?' I asked.

'And then, Danny, the child begins to dream a marvellous and fantastic dream... and when the dream reaches its most marvellous and fantastic moment... then the magic powder really takes over... and suddenly the dream is not a dream any longer but a real happening... and the child is not asleep in bed... he is fully awake and is actually in the place of the dream and is taking part in the whole thing... I mean really taking part... in real life. More about that tomorrow. It's getting late. Good night, Danny. Go to sleep.'

My father kissed me and then he turned down the wick of the little paraffin lamp until the

Do you think Danny's father is a good storyteller? Why?

flame went out. He seated himself in front of the wood stove which now made a lovely red glow in the dark room.

'Dad,' I whispered.

'What is it?'

'Have you ever actually seen The Big Friendly Giant?'

'Once,' my father said. 'Only once.'

'You did! Where?'

'I was out behind the caravan,' my father said, 'and it was a clear moonlit night, and I happened to look up and suddenly I saw this tremendous tall person running along the crest of the hill. He had a queer long-striding lolloping gait and his black cloak was streaming out behind him like the wings of a bird. There was a big suitcase in one hand and a blowpipe in the other,

and when he came to the high hawthorn hedge at the end of the field, he just strode over it as though it wasn't there.' ⭐

'Were you frightened, Dad?'

'No,' my father said. 'It was thrilling to see him and a little eerie, but I wasn't frightened. Go to sleep now. Good night.'

⭐ What words and phrases help to create the atmosphere on this page?

4

1. What do the letters BFG stand for?
2. What does the BFG do when he catches the dreams?
3. Describe how Danny's father smiled.

4. Danny and his father are very fond of each other. Find some words and phrases that show this.
5. What picture of the BFG do you get from this extract? What words and phrases help to create this picture for you?

6. Do you like the story of the BFG and his magic powders? Why?
7. Do you think Danny and his father live alone? Why do you think this?
8. How old do you think Danny is?
9. Is Danny a happy boy? Why do you think this?
10. How do you think children might react if they woke up while the BFG was blowing dreams into their bedroom?

11. Did your mother or father ever make up stories for you? Tell the class about one.
12. Do you remember your dreams? How do they make you feel?

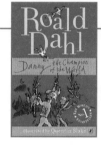

The Dream Keeper

Langston Hughes

Bring me all of your dreams,
You dreamers,
Bring me all of your
Heart melodies
That I may wrap them
In a blue cloud-cloth
Away from the too-rough fingers
Of the world.

Dreams

Langston Hughes

Hold fast to dreams
For if dreams die
Life is a broken-winged bird
That cannot fly.

Hold fast to dreams
For when dreams go
Life is a barren field
Frozen with snow.

1. Read the title of the extract and look at the illustrations. What do you think the story will be about? Make a prediction.
2. How often are the Olympic Games held?
3. Where were the most recent Olympic Games held? Where will the next ones be held?

Olympic Marathon

Morris Gleitzman

The TWENTY-SEVENTH Summer Olympics arrive in Australia – four years early!
'Manchester,' I pleaded softly. 'Please, let it be Manchester.'
Hoppy, my pet wallaby, stared at me as if I was mad, but I didn't care.
'Manchester,' I moaned desperately, 'or Beijing.'
I held my breath.
Hoppy held his.
The bloke on the telly announced that the Olympic Games in the year 2000 had been awarded to... Sydney.
Australia went bananas.
In our lounge room and across our town and up and down the state and right across the country people leapt out of their chairs and whooped with joy and hugged each other and their pets.
All except me.
I just sat there and watched Dad try to do a delighted cartwheel and crash into the electric bug zapper.
'Here we go,' I muttered to Hoppy. 'We're cactus, now.'
It started that evening.

Why do you think the boy doesn't want the games to be held in Australia?

8

I was drying up after tea when I heard Dad's voice behind me.

'A superb effort from the eleven-year-old,' he said. 'Look at that wiping action. This could be his personal best on the saucepan with lid.'

I sighed.

OK, Dad does a pretty good sports commentator's voice for an abattoir worker, but all I could think of was the 1,927 days to go till the Sydney Olympics.

'But wait!' yelled Dad. 'Look at this burst of speed from his nine-year-old rival. Fourteen point six three seconds for the non-stick frying pan. That's got to be close to a world record if she can get it on the shelf without dropping it.'

Sharon, my sister, rolled her eyes.

He was still at it two hours later when we were cleaning our teeth.

'It's Sharon, Sharon's holding on to her lead around the back teeth, but wait, she's slipped, her brush has slipped, oh no, this is a tragedy for the plucky youngster, she's missed a molar and Brendan has taken the lead, he's streaking home along the front ones, it's gold, it's gold, it's gold for Australia!'

Before we could remind Dad that shouting before bed gives kids nightmares, he herded us out into the backyard.

Sitting under the clothes hoist there were banana crates, the middle one taller than the others.

'The winners' podium,' announced Dad.

We stared, mouths open.

Dad had always been mad about sport, but he'd never gone this far.

Weak with shock, we allowed ourselves to be led up on to the podium, where Sharon received the silver medal for teeth cleaning and I was awarded the gold for dropping the frying pan. ⭐

Mum stuck her head out the back door.

'Bedtime, you kids,' she said. 'It's eight-fifteen.'

'Crossing now to the back door,' shouted Dad, 'to witness a true champion in action.'

Before she knew it, Mum was on the podium having an old beer bottle top on a ribbon hung round her neck for telling the right time.

Over the next days, gold medals were won at our place for potato peeling, TV watching, ironing, getting up in the morning, pet care, closing the fridge door, vacuuming, chess, whistling, putting socks on, toast scraping, yawning, homework, head scratching, microwave operation, hiccups, sleeping, nose picking, sitting down, standing up, walking, standing still, begging a parent to stop, and chucking a plastic strainer at a parent.

'Love,' Mum said to Dad as he was hanging another bottle top round her neck (spin

⭐ How did Brendan and Sharon react to their father's commentary?

9

dryer repairs), 'don't you think you're taking this a bit far?'
'Over to the spoilsports' stadium,' said Dad, 'where it looks like another gold for Australia!'
As the days turned into weeks, we all wanted to scream.
Finally Mum did. 'That's it!' she yelled. 'If I hear another mention of medals, Olympics or personal best time in the loo, I'll kill someone!'
Dad muttered something under his breath about gold, gold, gold for getting cranky, then did what he always did when Mum blew her stack.
Took us to visit Uncle Wal.
Uncle Wal lives three hours away on a sheep farm.
It's a really boring trip because the land's flat and scrubby, the road's dead straight and you hardly ever see another car. Plus, when you get there, Uncle Wal hasn't even got a telly.
But this trip wasn't boring.
Half-an-hour up the track we ran out of petrol.
'It's a gold for Australia,' said Sharon, 'for forgetting to fill the car up.'
Dad glared at her.
We waited for an hour.
No cars.
Finally, Dad got sick of giving us medals for waiting and set off on foot back to the petrol station in town.
For the next hour me and Sharon just enjoyed the silence.
Then I started to wish I had something to read.

Do you agree with Mum? How would you have reacted to Dad?

What else might Sharon have said?

I read the car manual, the soft drinks cans on the floor, and all the print on the dashboard, including the numbers.

Which is where I saw something very interesting.

I showed Sharon.

Then we saw a cloud of dust heading towards us.

It was Mrs Garwick from school in her van.

Soon we were speeding back to town.

After a bit I saw Dad in the distance, trudging along.

Mrs Garwick, who wears really thick glasses, hadn't seen him.

I distracted her attention by pretending to be sick in the back of the van.

She turned round, alarmed, and we sped past Dad.

Three hours later Dad staggered into town, hot, dusty and exhausted.

His shoulders drooped and he blinked painfully when he saw us sitting on the swings under a tree in the Memorial Park.

'Gold, gold, gold for Australia!' we yelled.

'Why didn't you stop for me?' croaked Dad.

Me and Sharon gave each other a puzzled frown.

'We thought you wanted to complete the distance on foot,' I said.

'Complete the distance!' shrieked Dad. 'It's forty kilometres.'

What might Brendan have seen?

'Forty-two point nine,' I said, hanging a gold bottle top round his neck.
'Let's hear it for Dad, gold medal winner in the Olympic marathon!'
That was the last Olympic gold medal anyone in our family won.
We're all glued to the telly, though, watching the real gold medals being won in Atlanta.
All except Dad.
He's gone to stay with Uncle Wal.

 How did Brendan know the exact distance?

1. What did Dad use as a.) a gold medal b.) a podium?
2. Why did Mrs Garwick not see Dad?

3. What do we learn about a.) Brendan b.) his father from the story? Find evidence from the extract to back up your opinion.
4. There is a lot of humour in this extract. Find some examples. Which did you find the funniest?
5. What impressions of Australia do you get from this extract?

6. Dad's mood changes during the story. Find where this happens.
7. Do you think Sharon and her Dad are alike? Give a reason to back up your opinion.
8. With which character would you sympathise most? Give a reason.
9. What role does Uncle Wal play in this story, do you think?
10. Did you expect the children to speed past their father in the van? How did the author build up to this?
11. If you were part of this family, what would you have done and why?

12. Why do countries want to host the Olympic Games?
13. The children's Dad imitated a sports commentator's voice. Choose a sport and make up a commentary for it.
14. There are different types of humour. Talk about them.

Fathers' Race

Brian Moses

Tony's dad goes jogging,
Gareth's dad lifts weights.
Leroy's dad's a stunt man.
Errol's dad jumps gates!

Trixie's dad plays football
for a fourth division team.
Rachel's dad's a sprinter,
fast and flash and lean.

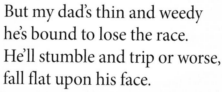

Simon Miller's dad
enters marathons.
I've seen him training hard,
Running from Simon's mum!

But my dad's thin and weedy
he's bound to lose the race.
He'll stumble and trip or worse,
fall flat upon his face.

I know my friends will laugh
and call me awful names.
Please don't enter the race, Dad,
it's me who gets the blame!

Can't be bothered to think of a title

Ian McMillan

When they make slouching in the chair
an Olympic sport
I'll be there.

When they give out a cup
for refusing to get up
I'll win it every year.

When they hand out the gold
for sitting by the fire
I'll leave the others in the cold,

and when I'm asked to sign my name
in the Apathetic Hall of Fame
I won't go.

Olympic excellence

1. Talk about the Olympic Games. Name some Irish Olympic athletes.
2. Have you watched any of the events? Which did you think was the most exciting?

Ancient times

The Greeks of ancient times worshipped many gods. The greatest of their gods was Zeus and every four years the Greeks held an athletics festival in his honour at Olympia. The first recorded Olympic Games were held in 776BC. There was just one event, the stade race, run over a distance of nearly 200 metres. The first Olympic champion was a cook. Over time, other events were introduced, including jumping, wrestling, chariot-racing, and spear and discus throwing. During the period of the games a sacred truce was proclaimed throughout Greece. Nothing, not even war, was allowed to interfere with the celebration of the Games. The Greeks believed that the Games were as much a religious as a sporting festival, and two days were devoted to religious ceremonies.

The prize for an Olympic champion was not a gold medal as it is today, but a wreath of olive leaves. Success brought instant fame to the athlete.

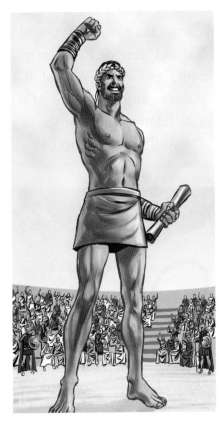

Temple of Hera in Olympia

Odes were written in his honour, statues were erected commemorating his victory and athletes did not have to pay taxes for the rest of their lives.

After the year 390AD the ancient games were discontinued. The Roman Empire had just become Christian. They looked upon the games as a pagan festival.

The modern games

The modern games date from 1896 and were very much the inspiration of the Frenchman, Baron Pierre de Coubertin. The first games in modern times were held in Athens, the capital of Greece. A total of 311 athletes took part, representing 13 nations. The most popular champion of the Athens games was a Greek shepherd, Spiridou Louis, who won the marathon. Since 1896, the Games have been held every four years, except for the years 1916, 1940 and 1944 when the world was at war.

The Olympic symbol

The symbol of the modern Olympic Games is five interlinked circles. These circles represent the five continents. The circles are linked to symbolise the cooperation and goodwill among all countries. The colours of the circles are red, green, blue, black and yellow. At least one of these colours is included in the flag of every country in the world.

The Olympic torch

The Olympic torch is lit by rays from the Sun at Olympia and is taken by relays of runners from there to wherever the Olympic Games are being held. The torch was introduced in 1934 by the International Olympic Committee.

Did you know?

Women were permitted to compete for the first time in the 1900 Olympics, but were only allowed to take part in lawn tennis and golf events. No women participated in the ancient Olympic Games. In fact, they weren't even allowed to watch. Women weren't allowed to take part in the athletics competitions until 1928.

Photo-finish cameras were introduced at the 1932 Games in Los Angeles, USA. An Olympic village was erected for the first time at these Games.

The 1936 Games in Berlin, Germany, were the first Olympics to be shown on television.

An Irishman, Lord Killanin, was President of the International Olympic Committee for many years.

The first Winter Olympic Games were held in France in 1924.

Some unusual events have been included in the Olympics over the years. In the 1896 Olympics, one of the competitions was the 100 metres swim for sailors. It was confined to members of the Greek navy!

The 1908 Games were switched from Rome to London because of the eruption of Mount Vesuvius in 1906. This was the first Olympics where athletes marched into the stadium behind their national flag.

The American ski jumper Anders Haugen had to wait 50 years for his medal. In the 1924 Winter Games an error in computing the score put him in fourth, rather than third, place. The mistake was not discovered until 1974. He received his bronze medal in a special ceremony that year!

The Paralympics are the Olympic Games contested by athletes with disabilities. They are held every four years in the same venue as the Olympic Games. In 2008, Ireland won five medals (three gold, one silver and one bronze) at the Beijing Paralympics in China. Jason Smyth won gold medals in the men's 100 and 200 metre events.

Karoly Takács, a soldier in the Hungarian army, was a member of the national pistol-shooting team. When his right hand was shattered by a grenade in 1938 he taught himself to shoot with his left hand, and he went on to win the gold medal in the rapid-fire pistol event in 1948 and 1952.

The USA have won more medals than any other country.

When Athens hosted the 2004 Games, the marathon race started in the town of Marathon, the starting point of the first ever marathon.

On 8 May 2008, the Olympic torch was carried by climbers to the 'roof of the world', when they reached the summit of Mount Everest. During the ascent, Tibetan women were the first and last to carry the torch.

Some famous Olympians

- The famous Irish painter Jack B. Yeats, brother of poet William Butler Yeats, was Ireland's first ever medallist at the Olympic Games – but not for sport! At the 1924 Olympic Games in Paris, France, there was an 'Arts and Culture' section. Yeats's painting '*The Liffey Swim*' won a silver medal. You can see this painting at the National Gallery in Dublin.
- Jesse Owens, an Afro-American, was the hero of the 1936 Games in Berlin, Germany. The German leader of the time, Adolf Hitler, attempted to use the Games to prove his theory of racial superiority. However, when Owens won four gold medals and was the most successful athlete of the Games, Hitler refused to present him with his medals.
- In 1948, Fanny Blankers-Koen, a Dutch athlete, was told by the press and her husband that she was 'too old' to compete

Jesse Owens at the 1936 Games in Berlin.

in the games even though she was just 30. She proved them wrong by winning four gold medals. She was one of the greatest athletes of the twentieth century being the first and only woman to win four gold medals at a single Olympics.

- Cassius Clay won the light heavyweight boxing title at the 1960 Games in Rome, Italy. He later became a famous professional boxer, better known as Muhammad Ali.
- The Ukrainian gymnast, Larissa Latynina was the first female athlete to win nine gold medals. These were won over three Games. In total, she has won 18 Olympic medals.
- At the 1976 Games, held in Montreal, Canada, Nadia Comaneci from Romania became the first gymnast in Olympic history to score a perfect 10. She was 14 years old at the time.
- At the 2000 Olympic Games in Sydney, Australia, Sonia O'Sullivan from Cobh, Co. Cork, considered one of Ireland's greatest ever athletes, won a silver medal in the 5,000 metre race.
- Ireland has performed very successfully in boxing events over the years. In the 2008 Games held in Beijing, China, Ireland won three Olympic medals – all in boxing. Kenneth Egan won a silver medal and Darren Sutherland and Paddy Barnes each won a bronze medal. Boxers have won nearly half of all Ireland's Olympic medals.
- Also at the 2008 Games, the American swimmer Michael Phelps won eight gold medals and broke eight world records! He set the record for the most number of gold medals won in a career. He has amassed 14 gold medals in total.

Sonia O'Sullivan

The marathon

The marathon is run over a distance of 40 kilometres and is a gruelling test of stamina and endurance. The race commemorates the heroic action of an Athenian named Pheidippides, who lived about 2,500 years ago. At that time, Greece was at war with the powerful kingdom of Persia. The small Athenian army defeated the mighty Persians at a place called Marathon. Pheidippides, who was the best runner among the Athenians, was chosen to run to Athens and proclaim the victory to the anxious citizens there. The distance from Marathon to Athens was about 40 kilometres. Pheidippides was weary after taking part in the battle, but he set off on his task without question. At the end of his exhausting ordeal, Pheidippides gasped out the good news that the city had been saved. He then collapsed and died on the spot. The first women's marathon took place at the Los Angeles Olympics in 1984.

The best of the Olympians

Below is a table of the most successful Olympic athletes. Examine it and answer the questions underneath.

No.	Athlete	Nation	Sport	Years	Games	Gender	Gold	Silver	Bronze	Total
1	Michael Phelps	United States	Swimming	2004–2008	Summer	M	14	0	2	16
2	Larisa Latynina	Soviet Union	Gymnastics	1956–1964	Summer	F	9	5	4	18
3	Paavo Nurmi	Finland	Athletics	1920–1928	Summer	M	9	3	0	12
4	Mark Spitz	United States	Swimming	1968–1972	Summer	M	9	1	1	11
5	Carl Lewis	United States	Athletics	1984–1996	Summer	M	9	1	0	10
6	Bjørn Dæhlie	Norway	Cross-country skiing	1992–1998	Winter	M	8	4	0	12
6	Birgit Fischer	Germany	Canoeing	1980–2004	Summer	F	8	4	0	12
8	Sawao Kato	Japan	Gymnastics	1968–1976	Summer	M	8	3	1	12
8	Jenny Thompson	United States	Swimming	1992–2004	Summer	F	8	3	1	12
10	Matt Biondi	United States	Swimming	1984–1992	Summer	M	8	2	1	11

1. Why do you think Larissa Latynina is not at the top of the table?
2. How many medals altogether did a.) Americans b.) Europeans win?
3. In which sport were the most medals won?
4. Which country in the table no longer exists? By what name is it known today?
5. Which athlete had the longest Olympic career?
6. Find out as much as you can about Irish men and women who have won Olympic medals.

The new and the old

Over the years many new sports have been added to the Olympic programme and to make way for them others have been discontinued.

Sport	First appearance
Football	1900 (Paris)
Boxing	1904 (St Louis)
Pentathlon	1912 (Stockholm)
Judo	1964 (Tokyo)
Softball (for women only)	1988 (Seoul)
Table tennis	1996 (Atlanta)
Taekwondo	2000 (Sydney)

Sport	Last appearance
Cricket	1900 (Paris)
Golf	1904 (St Louis)
Tug of war	1920 (Antwerp)
Rugby	1924 (Paris)
Polo	1936 (Berlin)
Baseball/softball	2012 (London)

1. Scan the unit and list all the information you can find about the 1936 Olympics.
2. What sport would you like to see a.) added to the Olympics and b.) dropped from the Olympics? Say why in each case.
3. Where were the Olympic Games held in each of these years:
   1896, 1904, 1912, 1920, 1932, 1960, 1964, 1976, 1980, 1996?

1. Before you read the introduction, look at the pictures. What do you think will happen in the extract?
2. Read the introduction. Does this help to set the scene for you?
3. Which of the three children do you think plays the biggest role in the extract?
4. What do you know about the Second World War?

NUMBER THE STARS

Lois Lowry

This story is set in Denmark during the Second World War. Annemarie Johansen's best friend, Ellen Rosen, is Jewish. The Jews in Denmark are being 'relocated' so Ellen has moved in with the Johansens and is pretending to be part of the family.

Chapter one: Why Are You Running?

'I'll race you to the corner, Ellen!' Annemarie adjusted the thick leather pack on her back so that her schoolbooks balanced evenly. 'Ready?' She looked at her best friend. Ellen made a face. 'No,' she said, laughing. 'You know I can't beat you – my legs aren't as long. Can't we just walk, like civilised people?' She was a stocky ten-year-old, unlike lanky Annemarie.

'We have to practise for the athletic meet on Friday – *I know* I'm going to win the girls' race this week. I was second last week, but I've been practising every day. Come on, Ellen,' Annemarie pleaded, eyeing the distance to the next corner of the Copenhagen street. 'Please?'

Ellen hesitated, then nodded and shifted her own rucksack of books against her shoulders. 'Oh, all right. Ready,' she said.

'Go!' shouted Annemarie, and the two girls were off, racing along the residential sidewalk. Annemarie's silvery blond hair flew behind her, and Ellen's dark pigtails bounced against her shoulders. ☆

'Wait for me!' wailed little Kirsti, left behind, but the two older girls weren't listening. Annemarie outdistanced her friend quickly, even though one of her shoes came untied as she sped along the street called Østerbrogade, past the small shops and cafés of her neighbourhood here in northeast Copenhagen. Laughing, she skirted an elderly lady in black who carried a shopping bag made of string. A young woman pushing a baby in a

☆ How is Ellen different from Annemarie?

22

carriage moved aside to make way. The corner was just ahead.

Annemarie looked up, panting, just as she reached the corner. Her laughter stopped. Her heart seemed to skip a beat.

'*Halte!*' the soldier ordered in a stern voice.

The German word was as familiar as it was frightening. Annemarie had heard it often enough before, but it had never been directed at her until now.

Behind her, Ellen also slowed and stopped. Far back, little Kirsti was plodding along, her face in a pout because the girls hadn't waited for her.

Annemarie stared up. There were two of them. That meant two helmets, two sets of cold eyes glaring at her, and four tall shiny boots planted firmly on the sidewalk, blocking her path to home.

And it meant two rifles, gripped in the hands of the soldiers. She stared at the rifles first. Then, finally, she looked into the face of the soldier who had ordered her to halt.

'Why are you running?' the harsh voice asked. His Danish was very poor. Three years, Annemarie thought with contempt. Three years they've been in our country, and still they can't speak our language.

'I was racing with my friend,' she answered politely. 'We have races at school every Friday, and I want to do well, so I –' Her voice trailed away, the sentence unfinished. Don't talk so much, she told herself. Just answer them, that's all.

Why do you think the soldier ordered Annemarie to stop?

She glanced back. Ellen was motionless on the sidewalk, a few yards behind her. Farther back, Kirsti was still sulking, and walking slowly toward the corner. Nearby, a woman had come to the doorway of a shop and was standing silently, watching.

One of the soldiers, the taller one, moved toward her. Annemarie recognised him as the one she and Ellen always called, in whispers, 'the Giraffe' because of his height and the long neck that extended from his stiff collar. He and his partner were always on this corner.

He prodded the corner of her backpack with the stock of his rifle. Annemarie trembled. 'What is in here?' he asked loudly. From the corner of her eye, she saw the shopkeeper move quietly back into the shadows of the doorway, out of sight.

'Schoolbooks,' she answered truthfully.

'Are you a good student?' the soldier asked. He seemed to be sneering.

'Yes.'

'What is your name?'

'Annemarie Johansen.'

'Your friend – is she a good student, too?' He was looking beyond her, at Ellen, who hadn't moved.

Annemarie looked back, too, and saw that Ellen's face, usually rosy-cheeked, was pale, and her dark eyes were wide. She nodded at the soldier. 'Better than me,' she said.

'What is her name?'

'Ellen.'

'And who is this?' he asked, looking to Annemarie's side. Kirsti had appeared there suddenly, scowling at everyone.

'My little sister.' She reached down for Kirsti's hand, but Kirsti, always stubborn, refused it and put her hands on her hips defiantly.

The soldier reached down and stroked her little sister's short, tangled curls. Stand still, Kirsti, Annemarie ordered silently, praying that somehow the obstinate five-year-old would receive the message.

But Kirsti reached up and pushed the soldier's hand away. '*Don't*,' she said loudly.

Both soldiers began to laugh. They spoke to each other in rapid German that

---

⭐ How is the sense of danger conveyed up to this point?

24

Annemarie couldn't understand.

'She is pretty, like my own little girl,' the tall one said in a more pleasant voice.

Annemarie tried to smile politely.

'Go home, all of you. Go study your schoolbooks. And don't run. You look like hoodlums when you run.'

The two soldiers turned away. Quickly Annemarie reached down again and grabbed her sister's hand before Kirsti could resist. Hurrying the little girl along, she rounded the corner. In a moment Ellen was beside her. They walked quickly, not speaking, with Kirsti between them, toward the large apartment building where both families lived. When they were almost home, Ellen whispered suddenly, 'I was so scared.'

'Me too,' Annemarie whispered back.

As they turned to enter their building, both girls looked straight ahead, toward the door. They did it purposely so that they would not catch the eyes or the attention of two more soldiers, who stood with their guns on this corner as well. Kirsti scurried ahead of them through the door, chattering about the picture she was bringing home from kindergarten to show Mama. For Kirsti, the soldiers were simply part of the landscape, something that had always been there, on every corner, as unimportant as lampposts throughout her remembered life.

'Are you going to tell your mother?' Ellen asked Annemarie as they trudged together up the stairs. 'I'm not. My mother would be upset.'

'No, I won't, either. Mama would probably scold me for running in the street.'

She said goodbye to Ellen on the second floor, where Ellen lived, and continued on to the third, practising in her mind a cheerful greeting for her mother: a smile, a

How has the girls' behaviour changed since their encounter with the soldiers?

Whose mother do you think would be more upset? Why?

25

description of today's spelling test, in which she had done well.

But she was too late. Kirsti had gotten there first.

'And he poked Annemarie's book bag with his gun, and then he grabbed my hair!' Kirsti was chattering as she took off her sweater in the centre of the apartment living room. 'But I wasn't scared. Annemarie was, and Ellen, too. But not me!'

Mrs Johansen rose quickly from the chair by the window where she'd been sitting. Mrs Rosen, Ellen's mother was there, too, in the opposite chair. They'd been having coffee together, as they did many afternoons. Of course it wasn't really coffee, though the mothers still called it that: 'having coffee'. There had been no real coffee in Copenhagen since the Nazi occupation. Not even any real tea. The mothers sipped at hot water flavoured with herbs.

'Annemarie, what happened? What is Kirsti talking about?' Her mother asked anxiously.

'Where's Ellen?' Mrs Rosen had a frightened look.

'Ellen's in your apartment. She didn't realise you were here,' Annemarie explained. 'Don't worry. It wasn't anything. It was just the two soldiers who stand on the corner of Østerbrogade – you've seen them; you know the tall one with the long neck, the one who looks like a silly giraffe?' She told her mother and Mrs Rosen of the incident, trying to make it sound humorous and unimportant. But their uneasy looks didn't change.

'I slapped his hand and shouted at him,' Kirsti announced importantly.

'No, she didn't, Mama,' Annemarie reassured her mother. 'She's exaggerating, as she always does.'

Mrs Johansen moved to the window and looked down to the street below. The Copenhagen neighbourhood was quiet; it looked the same as always: people coming and going from the shops, children at play, the soldiers on the corner.

She spoke in a low voice to Ellen's mother. 'They must be edgy because of the latest Resistance incidents. Did you read in *De Frie Danske* about the bombing in Hillerød and Nørrebro?'

Although she pretended to be absorbed in unpacking her schoolbooks, Annemarie listened, and she knew what her mother was referring to. *De Frie Danske – The Free Danes* – was an illegal newspaper; Peter Neilson brought it to them occasionally, carefully folded and hidden among ordinary books and papers, and Mama always burned it after she and Papa had read it. But Annemarie heard Mama and Papa talk, sometimes at night, about the news they received that way: news of sabotage against the Nazis, bombs hidden and exploded in the factories that produced war materials, and industrial railroad lines damaged so that the goods couldn't be transported.

And she knew what Resistance meant. Papa had explained, when she overheard the word and asked. The Resistance fighters were Danish people – no one knew who, because they were very secret – who were determined to bring harm to the Nazis however they could. They damaged the German trucks and cars, and bombed their factories. They were very brave. Sometimes they were caught and killed.

'I must go and speak to Ellen,' Mrs Rosen said, moving toward the door. 'You girls walk a different way to school tomorrow. Promise me, Annemarie. And Ellen will promise, too.'

'We will, Mrs Rosen. But what does it matter? There are German soldiers on every corner.'

'They will remember your faces,' Mrs Rosen said, turning in the doorway to the hall. 'It is important to be one of the crowd, always. Be one of many. Be sure that they never have reason to remember your face.' She disappeared into the hall and closed the door behind her.

Who do you think the Resistance were?

Can you imagine why Mrs Rosen said this?

1. Why did the children call one of the soldiers 'the Giraffe'?
2. Why did Annemarie want to have a race with Ellen?
3. Why has Ellen moved in with Annemarie's family?

4. There is a contrast in the extract between relaxed everyday happenings in the city and the tensions caused when there are soldiers about. Find some examples of each.
5. Kirsti plays an important part in the extract. What kind of girl is she? Find sentences from the extract that support your view/opinion.
6. What evidence is there from the extract that Annemarie is a thoughtful child?

7. The Jews in Denmark were being 'relocated'. What do you think this meant?
8. Which character plays the most important role in the extract?
9. How might Kirsti look back on this incident in later years?
10. What do you think life was like for the soldiers in the city? Why do you think this?
11. What do you think would happen if the illegal newspaper was found in their home?

12. Find out about the Resistance and about other countries that were occupied during the Second World War.
13. What do you know about Ireland's role in the war?

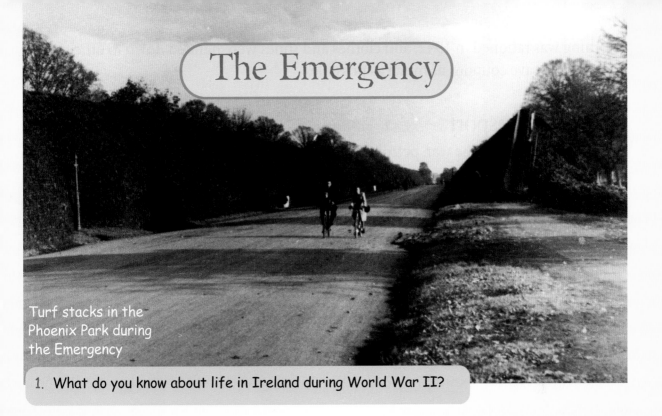

The Emergency

Turf stacks in the Phoenix Park during the Emergency

1. What do you know about life in Ireland during World War II?

In 1939, a great war broke out in Europe involving many countries. This was the second time in the 20th century that a war on such a large scale had been fought. It became known as World War II. Though Ireland was neutral, the war had an impact on daily life. In Ireland the war became known as the 'Emergency'.

Rationing

During the war, many everyday items were in short supply; some were not available at all. Because it was so difficult to import goods from other countries, many items were rationed. Rationing lasted until 1948. Ration books were issued to every family detailing the amount of food, fuel and clothes that they could buy each week. The books contained coupons which were given to the shopkeeper when rationed items were being bought.

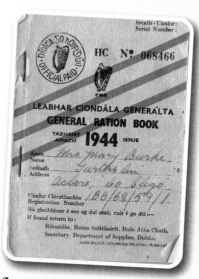

Tea, sugar, flour and butter were rationed at the outbreak of the war, with every person being allowed one ounce of tea and six ounces of butter per week. White flour was unavailable, so people had to eat poor quality bread, called 'black bread', made from home-grown flour.

The government encouraged people to be as self-sufficient as possible and to grow their own potatoes and vegetables. Crops were grown even in the Phoenix Park in Dublin.

Clothing was rationed in 1942, and clothes and shoes were handed down to other family members to save coupons as much as possible.

Fuel and transport

From the outbreak of the war, petrol was limited to essential services, including doctors, ambulances and public transport. Most people used bicycles to get around. Eventually, these were in short supply as rubber became scarce. Buses and trams were also affected by petrol rationing; the bus service finished at ten o'clock every night.

The train service also suffered, as engines that were designed to run on coal had to run on turf instead. This meant that journeys took much longer and there was only one train a day on all mainline routes.

The shortage of fuel meant that not as much electricity could be generated. Even the tram service was suspended in 1944, when severe drought reduced the output from the hydroelectric power-stations.

Cooking and heating

People were allowed to use gas for only a short time each day. In Dublin, a man called the 'glimmerman' went around to check that people did not cheat by using gas at other times. If the 'glimmerman' found that the gas ring was hot, the gas supply to that house would be cut off immediately.

Coal was also in short supply; many city-dwellers bought or rented plots of bogland and cut their own turf for fuel.

Irish shipping

During World War II, one of the greatest difficulties facing Ireland was that of importing food and raw materials. In 1941, the Irish government set up its own shipping company called Irish Shipping. Fifteen cargo ships were bought to carry the vital supplies from Britain and the US.

Every time the ships went to sea, the sailors knew that they were in danger, as there was a constant threat from German submarines, or 'U-Boats'. In 1942, the *Irish Pine* was sunk in the North Atlantic. All 33 sailors on board died. Neither the bodies nor the wreckage of the ship were ever found.

THE IRISH TIMES
MONDAY, SEPTEMBER 4, 1939

RESTRICTIONS ON TRAVELLING

CENSORSHIP OF LETTERS AND TELEGRAMS

Curfew May Be Imposed in Certain Cases

Regulations for Irish Shipping

The government at its meeting yesterday made a series of Orders under the new legislation passed by the Oireachtas at the sitting which concluded at a late hour yesterday morning.

The Minister for Justice may prohibit persons from leaving the country or entering it, or may impose such restrictions upon them as he thinks fit.

Persons travelling must provide themselves with passports and permits, whether going by rail, air or sea.

Irish ships must show only the Irish flag, and changes of registration must be approved by the Ministry of Industry and Commerce.

The Minister for Agriculture is empowered to take steps to maintain the production of essential products and for this purpose to require the cultivation of a minimum percentage of arable land. Provision is also made for the killing of rabbits to prevent injury to crops.

Provision of curfew in respect of certain areas is provided for, and no person shall be out of doors in such areas without a permit.

Another Order makes today (Monday) a bank holiday.

The Minister for Posts and Telegraphs is authorised to censor postal packets and telegrams, and the public are asked to conform to certain regulations with a view to facilitating this process.

CIVIL LIFE IN WAR-TIME

ENTERTAINMENTS CLOSED DOWN

People in Britain heard yesterday from the Lord Privy Seal that they should keep off the streets as much as possible, should carry gas masks always, and that places of entertainment and sport were to be closed.

1. Why do you think items such as coal, petrol and tea were scarce during the war?

2. Work out what the tea and butter ration would be in today's metric measurement.

3. Read the newspaper article above. Can you suggest a reason for each of the 'Orders'?

4. Look at the timeline on page 32. Research some facts about World War II and create your own timeline.

Timeline

Ireland	Date	World
	1939	
	1 September	Germany invades Poland
Ireland declares her neutrality	**2 September**	
	1940	
	May	Germany invades France; British evacuation from Dunkirk
German bombing of co-op in Campile, Co. Wexford; no one is killed	**August**	
	1941	
Two women killed by German bomb in Co. Carlow	**January**	
	April/May	Belfast is targeted in German bombing campaign; 700 die. Fire brigades from Dublin, Dundalk and Drogheda go to Belfast to help bring the fires under control.
27 die when the North Strand, Dublin is bombed	**May**	
	December	United States enter the war after the bombing of Pearl Harbour
	1942	
	February	American troops arrive in Northern Ireland
Sinking of the *Irish Pine*	**November**	
	June	British and American troops land in Sicily and southern Italy
	1944	
The tram service in Dublin is suspended	**June**	
	June	D-Day landings take place in France
	1945	
	8 May	Victory in Europe Day
	6 August	Bombing of Hiroshima
	14 August	Victory in Japan Day; war ends

War Games

John Foster

In a Star Wars T-shirt,
Armed with an Airfix bomber,
The young avenger
Crawls across the carpet
To blast the wastepaper basket
Into oblivion.

Later,
Curled on the sofa,
He watches unflinching
An edited version
Of War of the Day,
Only half-listening
As the newscaster
Lists the latest statistics.

Cushioned by distance
How can he comprehend
The real score?

Paying His Respects

John Foster

Great-Grandad never talked
About the war.
'That,' he'd say with a sigh,
'That's over and done with.'

When I asked him
If the war was like the wars
In comics and in films,
He simply said,
'No, it was real.'

Every year
He got out his medals
And joined the parade
To the cenotaph,
Paying his respects.

Unbearable!

Paul Jennings

Chapter one: Licked

1 Tomorrow when Dad calms down I'll own up. Tell him the truth. He might laugh.

He might cry. He might strangle me. But I have to put him out of his misery.

I like my dad. He takes me fishing. He gives me arm wrestles in front of the fire on cold nights. He plays Scrabble instead of watching the news. He tries practical jokes on me. And he keeps his promises. Always.

But he has two faults. Bad faults. One is to do with flies. He can't stand them. If there's a fly in the room he has to kill it. He won't use fly spray because of the ozone layer so he chases them with a fly swat. He races around the house swiping and swatting like a mad thing. He won't stop until the fly is flat. Squashed. Squished – sometimes still squirming on the end of the fly swat.

He's a dead-eye shot. He hardly ever misses. When his old fly swat was almost worn out I bought him a nice new yellow one for his birthday. It wasn't yellow for long. It soon had bits of fly smeared all over it.

It's funny the different colours that squashed flies have inside them. Mostly it is black or brown. But often there are streaks of runny red stuff and sometimes bits of blue. The wings flash like diamonds if you hold them up to the light. But mostly the wings fall off unless they are stuck to the swat with a bit of squashed innards.

2 Chasing flies is Dad's first fault. His second one is table manners. He is mad about manners.

35

And it is always my manners that are the matter.

'Andrew,' he says. 'Don't put your elbows on the table.'

'Don't talk with your mouth full.'

'Don't lick your fingers.'

'Don't dunk your biscuit in the coffee.'

This is the way he goes on every meal time. He has a thing about flies and a thing about manners.

Anyway, to get back to the story. One day Dad is peeling the potatoes for tea. I am looking for my fifty cents that rolled under the table about a week ago. Mum is cutting up the cabbage and talking to Dad. They do not know that I am there. It is a very important meal because Dad's boss, Mr Spinks, is coming for tea. Dad never stops going on about my manners when someone comes for tea.

'You should stop picking on Andrew at tea time,' says Mum.

'I don't,' says Dad.

'Yes you do,' says Mum. 'It's always "don't do this, don't do that." You'll give the boy a complex.' I have never heard of a complex before but I guess that it is something awful like pimples.

'Tonight,' says Mum. 'I want you to go for the whole meal without telling Andrew off once.'

'Easy,' says Dad.

'Try hard,' says Mum. 'Promise me that you won't get cross with him.'

Dad looks at her for a long time. 'Okay,' he says. 'It's a deal. I won't say one thing about his manners. But you're not allowed to either. What's good for me is good for you.'

'Shake,' says Mum. They shake hands and laugh.

I find the fifty cents and sneak out. I take a walk down the street to spend it before tea. Dad has promised not to tell me off at tea time. I think about how I can make him crack.

It should be easy. I will slurp my soup. He hates that. He will tell me off. He might even yell. I just know that he can't go for the whole meal without going crook. 'This is going to be fun,' I say to myself. ⭐

3 That night Mum sets the table with the new tablecloth. And the best knives and forks. And the plates that I am not allowed to touch. She puts out serviettes in little rings. All of this means that it is an important meal.

We don't usually use serviettes.

Mr Spinks comes in his best suit. He wears gold glasses and he frowns a lot. I can tell that he doesn't like children. You can always tell when adults don't like kids. They smile at you with their lips but not with their eyes.

Anyway, we sit down to tea. I put my secret weapon on the floor under the table. I'm

⭐ Make a prediction: Do you think the parents will be able to keep their promise?

sure that I can make Dad crack without using it. But it is there if all else fails.

The first course is soup and bread rolls. I make loud slurping noises with the soup. No one says anything about it. I make the slurping noises longer and louder. They go on and on and on. It sounds like someone has pulled the plug out of the bath. Dad clears his throat but doesn't say anything. I try something different. I dip my bread in the soup and make it soggy. Then I hold it high above my head and drop it down into my mouth. I catch it with a loud slopping noise. I try again with an even bigger bit. This time I miss my mouth and the bit of soupy bread hits me in the eye. Nothing is said. Dad looks at me. Mum looks at me. Mr Spinks tries not to look at me. They are talking about how Dad might get a promotion at work. They are pretending that I am not revolting.

The next course is chicken. Dad will crack over the chicken. He'll say something. He hates me picking up the bones.

The chicken is served. 'I've got the chicken's bottom,' I say in a loud voice.

Dad glares at me but he doesn't answer. I pick up the chicken and start stuffing it into my mouth with my fingers.

I grab a roast potato and break it in half. I dip my fingers into the margarine and put some on the potato. It runs all over the place.

I have never seen anyone look as mad as the way Dad looks at me. He glares. He stares. He clears his throat. But still he doesn't crack. What a man. Nothing can make him break his promise.

I snap a chicken bone in half and suck out the middle. It is hollow and I can see right through it. I suck and slurp and swallow. Dad is going red in the face. Little veins are standing out on his nose. But still he does not crack.

The last course is baked apple and custard. I will get him with that. Mr Spinks has stopped talking about Dad's promotion.

He is discussing something about discipline. About setting limits. About insisting on standards. Something like that. I put the hollow bone into the custard and use it like a straw. I suck the custard up the hollow chicken bone.

Dad clears his throat. He is very red in the face. 'Andrew,' he says.

He is going to crack. I have won.

'Yes,' I say through a mouth full of custard.

'Nothing,' he mumbles.

⭐ What do you imagine Mr Spinks is thinking?

⭐ Would you have cracked if you were Dad? Why?

Dad is terrific. He is under enormous pressure but still he keeps his cool. There is only one thing left to do. I take out my secret weapon.

4 I place the yellow fly swat on the table next to my knife.

Everyone looks at it lying there on the white tablecloth.
They stare and stare and stare. But nothing is said.
I pick up the fly swat and start to lick it. I lick it like an ice cream.
A bit of chewy, brown goo comes off on my tongue. I swallow it quickly. Then I crunch a bit of crispy, black stuff.
Mr Spinks rushes out to the kitchen. I can hear him being sick in the kitchen sink.
Dad stands up. It is too much for him. He cracks. 'Aaaaaagh,' he screams. He charges at me with hands held out like claws.
I run for it. I run down to my room and lock the door.
Dad yells and shouts. He kicks and screams. But I lie low.
Tomorrow, when he calms down, I'll own up. I'll tell him how I went down the street and bought a new fly swat for fifty cents.
I'll tell him about the currants and little bits of liquorice that I smeared on the fly swat.
I mean, I wouldn't really eat dead flies. Not unless it was for something important anyway. ⭐

⭐ How do you think Dad will react when he finds out the truth?

1. Why does Andrew think Mr Spinks does not like children?
2. What was Andrew's secret weapon?
3. Name Andrew's Dad's two faults.

4. What tense is this extract written in? What effect does this have?
5. What actions did Andrew take to make Dad crack?
6. How did the adults respond to Andrew's revolting behaviour?

7. Why do you think Andrew wanted to make his Dad crack?
8. Do you think Andrew would have behaved as badly if he had not overheard his parents' conversation in the kitchen?
9. Retell the story from the point of view of Mr Spinks.
10. Do you think Andrew's behaviour will affect his Dad's promotion? Why?
11. Do you think his Dad will try to explain to Mr Spinks what really happened?

12. What does it mean to have a complex about something?
13. Have you ever played a practical joke on someone? What happened?

The Centipede's Song

Roald Dahl

'I've eaten many strange and scrumptious dishes in my time,
Like jellied gnats and dandyprats and earwigs cooked in slime,
And mice with rice – they're really nice
When roasted in their prime.
(But don't forget to sprinkle them with just a pinch of grime.)

'I've eaten fresh mudburgers by the greatest cooks there are,
And scrambled dregs and stinkbugs' eggs and hornets stewed in tar,
And pails of snails and lizards' tails,
And beetles by the jar.
(A beetle is improved by just a splash of vinegar.)

'I often eat boiled slobbages. They're grand when served beside
Minced doodlebugs and curried slugs. And have you ever tried
Mosquitoes' toes and wampfish roes
Most delicately fried?
(The only trouble is they disagree with my inside.)

'I'm mad for crispy wasp-stings on a piece of buttered toast,
And pickled spines of porcupines. And then a gorgeous roast
Of dragon's flesh, well hung, not fresh –
It costs a pound at most,
(And comes to you in barrels if you order it by post.)

'I crave the tasty tentacles of octopi for tea
I like hot-dogs, I LOVE hot-frogs, and surely you'll agree
A plate of soil with engine oil's
A super recipe.
(I hardly need to mention that it's practically free.)

'For dinner on my birthday shall I tell you what I chose:
Hot noodles made from poodles on a slice of garden hose –
And a rather smelly jelly
Made of armadillo's toes.
(The jelly is delicious, but you have to hold your nose.)

'Now comes,' the *Centipede declared*, 'the burden of my speech:
These foods are rare beyond compare – some are right out
    of reach;
But there's no doubt I'd go without
A million plates of each
For one small mite,
One tiny bite
Of this FANTASTIC PEACH!'

Household inventions

1. When do you think the following were invented:
   a.) clock b.) telephone
   c.) radio d.) flushing toilet?
2. Tell the class about something you would like to invent.

Glass dates back to about 4000BC. It was made by melting silicon sand in a stone oven or kiln. In about 1500BC, the first glass containers were made by the Egyptians.

The first computers were made in the United States in the 1940s and were huge machines. They cost thousands of dollars to buy. The giant computer Colossus was used as a code-breaker during World War II. Computers were later used in factories (robotics), in business and for home entertainment.

The first domestic refrigerator was invented in 1879 by a German engineer called Carl von Linde. The refrigerator, which was a wooden box, was cooled by ice. The ice-man would deliver a huge block of ice to the ice-box in the kitchen. The first electric refrigerator arrived in the 1920s.

In 1895, radio signals were first broadcast over a distance of 1.2 kilometres by Guglielmo Marconi, an Irish-Italian engineer, in Bologna, Italy. At first messages were sent using Morse code. Marconi later helped to develop voice broadcasts. In 1919, the first voice broadcast across the Atlantic was made from Ballybunion, Co. Kerry to Nova Scotia in Canada.

In 1969, Klass Compaan, a Dutch scientist, invented the Compact Disk (CD). Phillips and Sony both bought the manufacturing rights in 1980. By 1986, more than 1,000,000 CD players had been sold.

In 1589, a man called Harrington built the first flushing toilet for Queen Elizabeth I of England. It was called a water-closet and it was connected to outside drains. In 1884, Thomas Crapper developed the modern toilet.

The first bathtub dates back to around 1800BC. It was found in Babylonia (modern Iraq). In Roman times people went to public baths, where they could have hot and cold baths and other beauty treatments.

The telephone was invented in 1876 by Alexander Graham Bell. Ireland's first telephone exchange was opened in 1880. Only five telephones were connected to the exchange!

The Egyptians first measured time with water clocks and shadow clocks. Christian Huygens invented the first accurate pendulum clock in 1656.

Television was invented in 1925 by a Scotsman, John Logie Baird. At first, pictures were seen only in black and white. On 31 December 1961, Telefís Éireann began broadcasting from its studios in Dublin.

Dr Martin Cooper is thought to be the inventor of the mobile phone. It was first tried out on the public in 1977, in Chicago on a group of 2,000 people. Today, there are as many mobile phones in Ireland as there are people.

In 2001, the Apple Corporation developed and launched an invention that changed the way people could access and listen to music: the iPod, a portable media player. Steve Jobs, Apple CEO, announced that it put '1000 songs in your pocket'.

1. Choose another household invention. Find out when and where it was invented.
2. What do you think is the best invention of the last 100 years?
3. What do you think might be invented in the next century?

43

The Alien

Irene Yates

Narrator	It is Saturday night and the Holly family are having their usual argument about what they are going to watch on the television.
Ben	I want to watch *Night of the Aliens*.
Tracey	Well, you can't. Mum and I want to watch *Special Hospital*. So there.
Ben	Dad said I could choose this week.
Dad	Yes, I did. I remember telling him, last Saturday. We were all watching *Special Hospital* – just because you and Mum wanted to watch it – and I said Ben could choose this week.
Mum	That's only because you knew what he'd choose!
Tracey	Well, I don't want to watch a pointless science fiction film.
Ben	It's not a pointless film. It's really good. Everybody's seen it except us. It's got all these creatures from outer space in it –

Tracey	Creatures from outer space!
Mum	No such thing!
Dad	Come on – you don't know that…
Ben	… and brilliant special effects…
Tracey	It's ridiculous – lots of actors running around in daft costumes…
Mum	Not as good as *Special Hospital*…
Ben	It's won film awards…
Dad	Okay. Okay. Tell you what. Let's toss for it. Heads we watch *Night of the Aliens*. Tails, it's *Special Hospital*.
Narrator	Ben tosses a coin. It lands heads up.
Ben	Yeah!
Tracey	Oh no!
Mum	Never mind, love. We can always video our programme and watch it later.
Ben	You never know – you might enjoy it.
Narrator	Tracey pulls a face at him. The family settle down on the sofa and switch on *Night of the Aliens*. To Mum and Tracey's surprise they get engrossed in it. They just get to the part when the alien goes into the house when there is a Bang! Bang! Bang! on their front door.
Dad	Who on earth can that be at this time of night? Someone go and see who it is.
Mum	Well, it won't be for me. It's probably one of Ben's friends. You go, Ben.
Ben	All my friends will be at home watching the film. It must be for Tracey. Tracey, you go.
Tracey	It won't be for me. All my friends will be at home watching *Special Hospital*. I'm not going.
Narrator	There is another loud bang on the door.
Dad	I don't care who it is. Will one of you go and answer that door!
Narrator	Mum, Ben and Tracey all make for the door at once. They open it.

Mum Ben Tracey	*(loudly)* AAAHHHH!!!
Tracey	*(gasping)* Oh my goodness!
Narrator	Standing in the doorway is a huge green alien.
Alien	Gloddop!
Tracey	Help! What is it?
Mum	Dad! I think it's somebody for you! You'd better come here, quickly.
Ben	Quick Dad!
Narrator	Dad comes to see what the noise is about.
Dad	What's going on?
Narrator	He sees the alien filling up the doorway.
Dad	What… what… what's that?

Alien	Gloddop!
Mum	Well, don't just stand there! Are we going to ask it in or what?
Dad	Shut the door on it, quickly. Let it go somewhere else!
Narrator	Mum, Ben and Tracey try to shut the door but the alien holds up its arm and the door disappears.
Mum	Now look what it's done!
Alien	Gloddop!
Mum	I think we'd better let it come in.
Dad	Well, hurry up! Before the neighbours start to wonder what is going on. Bring it in.
Narrator	They all walk backwards into the living room with the alien following them. They all sit down on the sofa. The alien squeezes in between Mum and Dad.
Alien	Gloddop!
Tracey	How do we know if it's friendly?
Dad	We don't.
Ben	It looks friendly to me.
Mum	We could ask it.
Dad	Go on then.
Narrator	Mum turns to the alien. She gives it a friendly smile and says…
Mum	Are you a friend?
Alien	Gloddop! Gloddop!
Mum	It doesn't understand me. Ben, you try.
Narrator	Ben gets up off the sofa and speaks to the alien in a robotic kind of voice.
Ben	I – Ben. I – friend. You?
Alien	Gloddop!
Ben	There, you see. It says its name is Gloddop.

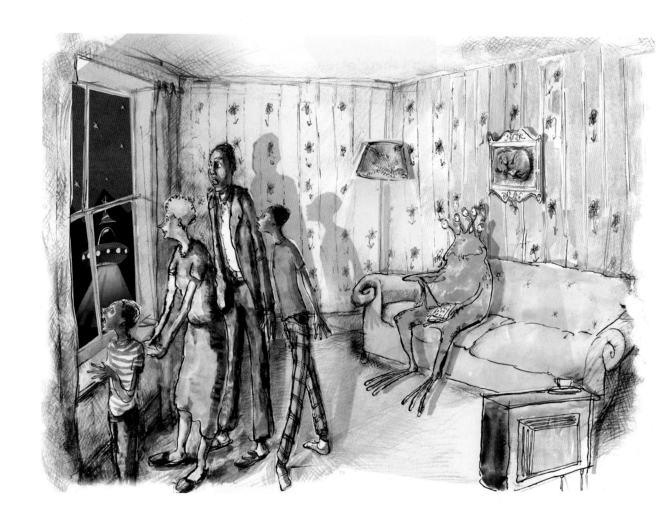

Dad	It says 'Gloddop' to everything. Tracey, you're good with animals and things. You try.
Narrator	Tracey gets up off the sofa and kneels in front of the alien. She puts her hands out to it and speaks in a sing-song kind of voice.
Tracey	Me, Tracey. Me like you. You like me?
Alien	Gloddop! Gloddop! Gloddop!
Mum	There! It does like our Tracey. It must be friendly.
Narrator	Mum puts her hand out to the alien, so that they can shake hands. She gives it her warm, comforting smile.
Mum	How do you do? We're very pleased to meet you. I'm Mrs Holly. These are my children, Ben and Tracey Holly. And this is my husband, Mr Holly.
Narrator	Dad stands up and puts out his hand. The alien takes it, holds it tightly and shakes it firmly up and down.

Dad	Well. It's very nice to meet you. I must say, we don't get many like you around these parts.
Narrator	The alien at last lets go of Dad's hand. Dad puts it behind his back, trying not to let everybody see him wince.
Ben	(*in his robotic voice*) Can – you – tell – us – where – you – come – from?
Alien	Gloddop!
Tracey	That's nice. It comes from Gloddop.
Mum	Is that as far as Mars, or not?
Dad	It's probably further.
Ben	I wonder how it got here. (*to the alien*) How – you – come – here?
Narrator	The alien nods towards the window.
Alien	Gloddop – gloddop.
Narrator	Ben looks out of the window. There is a flying saucer on the road in front of their house.
Ben	There's a flying saucer out there.
Narrator	Mum takes a look.
Mum	The neighbours won't like the alien parking there.
Dad	Well, we can't do anything about it. They'll just have to put up with it.
Tracey	I wonder how long it's staying.
Ben	Ask it.
Tracey	(*in her sing-song voice*) You stay here long? How long?
Alien	Gloddop!
Mum	Oh, that's all right then. It won't be here long enough to upset anybody.
Dad	I suppose, when it's gone, I'll have to find the front door and put it back on.
Ben	If you left the door off it would save us having to answer it all the time.
Dad	That's true. Good idea.
Narrator	They all sit back down to carry on watching the television. In the film, the alien begins to pick out the humans, one by one, and exterminate them. The family feel a bit uncomfortable and they all begin to fidget.

Mum	Perhaps it's time I made some sandwiches.
Narrator	Mum turns to the alien.
Mum	I bet you would like something to eat, wouldn't you?
Alien	Gloddop!
Mum	You see? It's probably starving. Poor thing! Ben, come and help me.
Ben	Do I have to?
Dad	Go on Ben. It's your turn.
Narrator	Mum goes into the kitchen and Ben follows her, pulling a face. When they come back, Tracey and Dad have disappeared.
Alien	Burp!

I'm Being Abducted by Aliens

Jack Prelutsky

I'm being abducted by aliens,
and I'm not enjoying the ride.
They simply appeared in their saucer
and beamed me directly inside.
It's creepy and weird in this saucer,
a strange sort of purplish brown,
I can't tell the floor from the ceiling,
in fact, I may be upside down.

The aliens have odd little bodies,
a cross between melons and eggs.
Their hands end in hundreds of tendrils,
they don't seem to have any legs.
They don't seem to have any noses,
they don't seem to have any eyes,
instead, on their heads are medallions
that keep changing colour and size.

They're feeding me gloppy concoctions
that taste even worse than they look.
I guess, since they're totally mouthless,
they don't need to know how to cook.
They haven't revealed where we're going,
or why we are taking this tour.
This unannounced alien abduction
is making me feel insecure.

As we hurtle on through the cosmos,
I'm breathing unbreathable air,
yet all my complaints go unheeded,
my alien abductors don't care.
But now I've a pressing dilemma
that simply cannot be ignored,
I'm dying to go to the bathroom –
they don't seem to have one on board.

51

1. Read the Jack Prelutsky poems on pages 51 and 55.
2. Look at the headings in this piece. What do you think they might be about?

Getting started

Jack Prelutsky was born in New York in 1940. As a school boy he disliked poetry and was much more interested in drawing. He worked as a truckdriver, photographer, folksinger and at other jobs before discovering his true talent as a poet. The following extract shows how he got started. He submitted some drawings to a publisher and wrote poems to go with them.

Will write for shelter

And I said, 'Really? You mean you like my drawings?'

She said, 'Oh, no. You're the worst artist I've ever seen, but you have a natural gift here for writing rhyme and verse.'

I said, 'But Miss Hirschman, I worked for six months on these drawings and two hours on these poems.'

She says, 'Well, that doesn't matter. You're no good at this. You're very good at that.'

And I said, 'You really like my poems?'

She said, 'Yes.'

I said, 'That's wonderful. Pay me.'

She said, 'Well, no. It doesn't work that way. This book is a little far-out. Do you think you could write about real animals?'

Well, it happens that I grew up in the Bronx, and I spent a lot of time when I was a kid going to the Bronx Zoo. Yes, I thought, I could write about real animals. She had me coming in about once a week. I was about 23 years old, and I'd bring her whatever animal poems I'd written. She had a little drawer just for me in her desk. Maybe I'd give her seven poems. She'd keep one, throw the other six out, put that one in her drawer, and then she'd take me to lunch. It would be the only decent meal I'd have in that week.

Well, after months and months of this, we were close to a book, and she took me to a really wonderful lunch and said, 'Jack, I think we need five more poems to do a book.'

I was in despair. I didn't think I had another poem in me. But I went back down to my illegal living situation – I was living in a commercial loft illegally – and there was a notice on the door – big red letters on white. It said essentially, 'PAY UP OR GET OUT – 24 HOURS. THIS MEANS YOU.' It might have been 48 hours. It was from the US marshal.

Well, sometimes people ask me what motivates me. That was a motivator! I went to my friend Harry's house and got about two quarts of black coffee, went back to the loft, and I started writing. I stayed up all night, and didn't sleep at all. By morning, I had written six poems.

It was a Friday. I had no money. I had to walk to the publisher. I didn't make an appointment, because I couldn't call the publisher. My phone had been disconnected. So, I walked into the publisher, stormed in, and said, 'Susan, here are six poems. Take 'em or leave 'em.'

She looked at them and said, 'Wow. This one, this one, this one, this one, and this one. This one's not so good. We have a book!'

'We have a book? That's wonderful. Pay me.'

In the following extract Prelutsky gives us an insight into how he approaches writing.

Stacks of notebooks

I'm never without a notebook. I have one here. I wear cargo pants a lot, so it's easier for me to slip a notebook in. I always carry a notebook and at least two pens, in case one runs out of ink. I'm a compulsive note taker.

As it happens, last night I couldn't sleep. I woke up at 3:15, and I went into the bathroom of our hotel room so as not to wake my wife. I turned on the light and put the seat down on the toilet, sat down, and I wrote a poem of three verses that's for New Kid Number Five that I'm working on right now – a book that has no other title yet. It's about two dragons a little too macho for their own good. What happens when dragons meet and neither of them likes the other? I wrote that last night between three and five in the morning. So, I'm always writing.

I do most of my finish work at home. I've learned to write everywhere. I write in hotels. I write in restaurants. I write on airplanes. But sooner or later, I have to get it down so it's legible and do the fine work, the tweaking. I do that at home. I work on a computer, so I have to do that.

But I have taken so many notes over the years. I have a stack of notebooks now that, if you piled them up, they would probably go way past the ceiling. I've been doing it for about 40 years, and I have a couple of drawers in a fire-resistant safe filled with them. I have this fear that I'll lose them, and I still haven't culled them. There are ideas I haven't touched yet from 30 or 40 years ago. I'm going to have to cull them to do this next book, because I'm running out of new ideas.

1. Discuss what you learned about Jack Prelutsky in the unit.
2. You can hear Jack Prelutsky speak and learn more about his work on the following website: www.readingrockets.org/books/interviews/Prelutsky
3. Research another poet using the library or internet. In your report include some information about the poet's life and some poems. Present it to the class.

Nine Mice

Jack Prelutsky

Nine mice on tiny tricycles
went riding on the ice,
they rode in spite of warning signs,
they rode despite advice.

The signs were right, the ice was thin,
in half a trice, the mice fell in,
and from their chins down to their toes,
those mice entirely froze.

Nine mindless mice, who paid the price,
are thawing slowly by the ice,
still sitting on their tricycles
... nine white and shiny micicles!

Prepare for take-off

1. List different methods of transport. Which ones do you like and which ones do you dislike? Why?

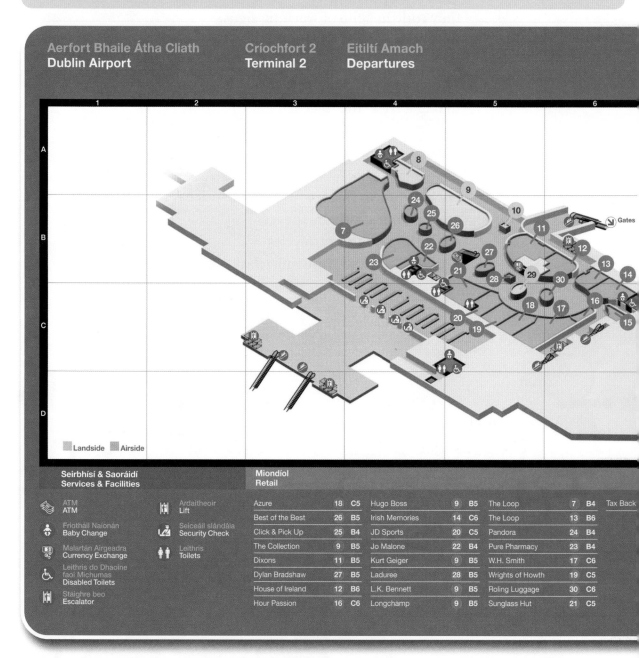

Aerfort Bhaile Átha Cliath
Dublin Airport

Críochfort 2
Terminal 2

Eitiltí Amach
Departures

Landside Airside

Seirbhísí & Saoráidí
Services & Facilities

ATM — ATM
Fríotháil Naíonán — Baby Change
Malartán Airgeadra — Currency Exchange
Leithris do Dhaoine faoi Míchumas — Disabled Toilets
Staighre beo — Escalator
Ardaitheoir — Lift
Seiceáil slándála — Security Check
Leithris — Toilets

Miondíol
Retail

Azure	18	C5	Hugo Boss	9	B5	The Loop	7	B4	Tax Back
Best of the Best	26	B5	Irish Memories	14	C6	The Loop	13	B6	
Click & Pick Up	25	B4	JD Sports	20	C5	Pandora	24	B4	
The Collection	9	B5	Jo Malone	22	B4	Pure Pharmacy	23	B4	
Dixons	11	B5	Kurt Geiger	9	B5	W.H. Smith	17	C6	
Dylan Bradshaw	27	B5	Laduree	28	B5	Wrights of Howth	19	C5	
House of Ireland	12	B6	L.K. Bennett	9	B5	Roling Luggage	30	C6	
Hour Passion	16	C6	Longchamp	9	B5	Sunglass Hut	21	C5	

Airports are very busy places. Every day thousands of people pass through our airports and many planes land and take off. The busiest airport in Ireland is Dublin airport. In 2010, over 18 million passengers passed through the airport. That's more than 50,000 a day! Seventy-eight airlines operate from it to more than 200 destinations!

Passengers need to arrive at the airport in plenty of time for their flight. The building they go to at the airport is called the terminal. In some airports there is one main terminal. In other airports there are different terminals for different destinations. Inside each terminal, there is a departures area where there are many check-in desks. There is a different check-in desk for each destination and each airline.

Check in

At the airline check-in desk, passengers must show their tickets and sometimes their passports. Each passenger is then given a boarding pass. At the same time, passengers check in their heavy suitcases or bags. Each bag is weighed and tagged and placed on a conveyor belt. The tags carry the flight code number and the airport destination. The conveyor belt takes all the baggage to the baggage handling area. Here, baggage handlers pack the pieces of baggage into containers and transport them to the aircraft.

Many travellers today prefer to check in on-line. They are issued their boarding passes in the comfort of their own homes and are able to avoid queues at the airport. There are also self-service check-in points at the airport, again designed to avoid long queuing.

Security

After check-in, passengers have to go through security checks. This means that they walk through a metal detector frame, which detects anything made of metal, from coins and keys to hospital pins and plates attached to bones. If guns, knives or explosives are detected, these are confiscated immediately and the passenger is taken aside for questioning. X-ray machines are used to check hand luggage. Passengers are advised to bring only what they need in their hand luggage. The remainder should go in their check-in luggage. The hand luggage is checked by electronic equipment and may also be subject to a hand search.

Containers of liquids such as shampoo, water, gels, etc, must not hold more than 100 millilitres if they are to be taken on board as hand luggage. These liquids must be placed in transparent, resealable bags, for ease of inspection.

Departure

Aircraft are parked in special places outside the terminal building. Each parking place has a gate number. Passengers wait in the departure lounge until their flight is called. While waiting they may have something to eat or drink or they may do some shopping. When their flight is called, passengers go to their gate. Here their boarding passes and passports are checked and they are allowed onto the plane. As passengers enter the aircraft, airline staff check their boarding passes again. They count the passengers to make sure no-one is missing.

Terminal 2 at Dublin Airport opened in November 2010

Checklist for take-off

You may need these things for your flight:

- Passport
- Boarding pass
- Hand baggage
- Return ticket
- Foreign currency

There are more than 10,000 people working in Dublin airport. They do a variety of jobs to help the airport run smoothly – from the airport police and fire service, who operate 24 hours a day every day of the year, to the trolley attendants who are responsible for over 4,000 trolleys.

1. In which countries would you find these airports:
   a.) Charles de Gaulle   c.) Marco Polo
   b.) Leonardo da Vinci   d.) John Lennon?

2. Find other airports that are named after famous people.

3. If you worked in an airport, what job would you like to have? Why? Tell the class your reasons.

4. How many airlines can you name?

5. Look at the plan of the departure area, why might you use each of these before going on a flight? a.) pharmacy b.) currency exchange c.) ATM

6. Look at the grid references on the plan. What can be found in C4? B6? A4?

7. Name and locate some other Irish airports.

The Vampire Vanishes

Willis Hall

Count Alucard is a vegetarian vampire from Transylvania. He has decided to take a quiet break and visit a friend in England. In this extract, the Count's plane has just landed and he is trying to clear Customs.

Chapter two

'We'll have that coffin up on the counter, as quickly as you please!' growled the Customs officer. 'Open up the lid and let's be seeing what you've got inside.'
'My dear young man, I am only too happy to oblige,' murmured the Count, hoisting the coffin from off the trolley and onto the inspection counter with the same ease that he had lifted it up from the luggage carousel. He tugged at the heavy polished lid which opened with an eerie creak that sent goose-pimples up, then down, the Customs officer's spine.

One by one, the Count lifted out the items which were in the coffin and laid them neatly, in a row, on the counter.

The coffin's satin-lined interior held all of those personal belongings which the Count considered essential for an overseas journey: a couple of starched white frilly-fronted shirts, both bearing the monogram 'C-A'; several items of white silk underwear, similarly embroidered; a pair of crimson pyjamas with the same family crest on the jacket pocket; some pairs of black silk socks; a toilet-bag for his toothbrush, toothpaste, shaving things and a bottle of his favourite aftershave, *Transylvanian Dawn*, which smelled both of pine trees in the early morning and woodland bracken heavy with dew; a six-pack of cans of tomato juice; some embrocation, containing secret ingredients, to keep his parchment-like bat-wings supple; and, last but by no means least, the latest issue of *The Coffin-Maker's Journal* (which was his constant bedside reading).

Customs Officer Hilton Hargreaves pursed his lips, frowned, and studied all of these items in turn, without saying a word. ✧

'May I put them back now, please?' asked the Count, politely, when he judged that the Customs man had completed his inspection.

'Certainly not!'

'May I ask, *why* not?'

'Empty your pockets first.'

Count Alucard sighed, but did as he was told. He laid out the contents of his pockets alongside the items from the coffin: his wallet; his cheque book from the Bank of Transylvania; his passport; his airline ticket; his bunch of keys including the clumsy, iron-cast ancient key that turned the lock of Castle Alucard's iron-studded oak front door. There was not one single item to which the Customs officer could raise the slightest objection, but he did not appear any happier. 'It all seems very suspicious to me,' he

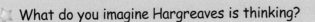

✧ What do you imagine Hargreaves is thinking?

grumbled. 'How am I to know that there isn't a secret panel or a false bottom in that coffin?'

'My name is Alucard,' declared the Count, proudly drawing his thin frame up to its full height. 'I am *Count* Alucard. I come from a noble Transylvanian family which stretches back across the centuries. A sliding panel? A false bottom? Believe me, sir, I would not so much as countenance either one of those subterfuges inside *my* coffin.'

'So *you* say,' replied Hargreaves from behind his counter.

'But how am I to know whether you are telling me the truth or whether it's a whopping great fib?'

'Because I am a man of my word,' said the Count. 'Examine that coffin to your heart's content – you will find nothing untoward.' Then, taking hold of his cloak on either side with both of his hands, he spread them wide on either side of his body. 'You have all of my possessions in front of you,' he said. 'But search me too if you don't believe me.'

'I'm sure that won't be necessary,' mumbled the Customs officer.

The truth of the matter was, of course, that Hilton Hargreaves was unable to step out from behind his counter. To have done so would have been to reveal the fact that, although the upper part of his body was smartly clothed in his Customs officer's uniform, his feet were contained in the panda slippers.

'I'm staying exactly where I am,' the Customs man continued to the Count. There was no way that he was going to display Aunt Edith's slippers to a member of the general public.

To tell the honest truth, Hilton Hargreaves was beginning to feel just a little bit ashamed of himself for the bad-tempered way he had treated the passenger. After all, the Customs officer admitted to himself, it wasn't a *crime* to use a coffin as a suitcase – it was just a little unusual, that was all.

'I'll tell you what, sir,' said Hilton Hargreaves, picking up the Count's passport. 'If your travel documents are in order, you can push off with the coffin and we'll say no more about it.'

'Why, thank you,' said the Count, delighted that his ordeal was almost over.

As the Customs officer flicked through the Transylvanian passport with its impressive gold-embossed double-headed eagle's insignia, the Count loaded his clothing back inside the coffin and put his other bits and pieces in his pockets.

'I'd say that's okey-dokey, sir,' said Officer Hargreaves, handing back the passport with a smile.

> As you read, look out for where Hargreaves' attitude begins to change. Why do you think it changes?

'Thanks very much – I am indebted to you,' said Count Alucard as he heaved his coffin back onto the trolley.

'Have a nice day!' called Hilton Hargreaves as the Count moved off, trundling the trolley towards the airport lounge.

Seconds later, after the Count had been swallowed up in the waiting throng, the Customs officer started to have second thoughts. A sixth sense began to tell him that there had been something slightly dodgy about the black-cloaked traveller, if only he could put his finger on it… The Customs officer tugged at the lobe of his left ear – a sign that he was thinking hard – and pondered over the several minutes he had spent questioning the man. 'What was his name again?' Hargreaves asked himself. 'Something beginning with "A",… Allanby…? Atkinson…? Abercrombie…? No.' And then, all at once, it came to him. 'Alucard!' Yes, that was it! '*Count* Alucard!'

All at once, the Customs officer felt the short hairs on the back of his neck bristle against the inside of his uniform shirt-collar. He sucked in his breath and then let it out again in a long, low whistle. The awful truth had struck him, hard.

'ALUCARD' was 'DRACULA' backwards! And suddenly everything seemed to fall into place! Everything from why the man had carried his belongings in a coffin down to why he went around in a frilly white shirt, a black bow tie, a posh black suit and a crimson-lined black cloak. And – yes! – now that he came to think of it, the man had two pointy vampire teeth, one on either side of his mouth!

As if all of that was not proof

enough, Hilton Hargreaves suddenly remembered that Count Alucard had handed him a Transylvanian passport. All vampires came from Transylvania. Hargreaves knew that for a certain fact.

With shaking hands, Hilton Hargreaves flicked through the pages of the Undesirable Visitors file. He turned to the page which contained, in alphabetical order, the names of all those frightening people which began with a 'D'. He ran his forefinger down the list:

DALEKS

DEADLY POISONOUS SNAKES

DOCTOR CRIPPEN (Deceased)

DOCTOR FRANKENSTEIN

DOCTOR FRANKENSTEIN'S MONSTER

DRACULA (Count)…

The Customs officer's forefinger began to shake more than ever. What was worse, beside the name there was an added entry in pencil: 'Not to be granted entry into the United Kingdom *under any circumstances* whatsoever. Signed J.P. Cazelot, Chief Customs Officer.'

'Oh, crumbs!' murmured Hargreaves to himself. 'Now I am in real hot water!'

⭐ Hargreaves is a gullible character. Do you agree? Why?

1. Name some of the things that were in Count Alucard's pocket.
2. Why was Hargreaves unable to step out from behind the counter?
3. Why was Count Alucard travelling to England?

4. List the things which convinced Hargreaves that Alucard was a vampire.
5. Count Alucard uses formal language. Hargreaves on the other hand uses informal language. Find examples of each in the text.
6. This is a far-fetched story. What details contribute to this?

7. Why do you think Hargreaves was wearing slippers?
8. In pairs act out the conversation that takes place between Hargreaves and the customs officer when they meet again.
9. What do you think will happen next? Why?

10. What items might each of the following have in their luggage: a.) an eight year-old child b.) a school teacher c.) a writer d.) a detective e.) an athlete?
11. Create the front page headline for *The Coffin Maker's Journal*.

Dracula

Jackie Kay

After we'd climbed the many roads for Efori Nord
by bus past Bucharest, the capital of Romania,
I was dog tired. We went to a mountain room of pine,

and I searched the cupboards before I fell asleep.
That night I heard this weird flapping
at the window and woke up scared to death.

There, on the veranda, was a figure in black.
Casting no shadow. My hand instinctively flew
to my neck. Count Dracula was born here.

The cotton sheets were soaking with my sweat.
I could see his eyes flashing as he bent down;
imagine two small sinister holes in my skin.

If only we had stayed in Efori Nord,
playing ping-pong till kingdom come.
If only we hadn't come to the mountains.

I crawled along the pine floor to my father's bed.
It was empty. Just a white pillow and a headrest.
My dad gave a loud guffaw from the balcony.

Took off his black cape; threw back his head,
said, 'Got you going there, didn't I?
Okay. The joke's over. Back to your bed.'

Can you believe that? All I am asking is:
who needs an imagination, a fear, or a dread,
when what we've got is parents instead?

Monsters and vampires

1. What is the scariest book you've ever read? Talk about it.
2. Make a list of all the spooky words you can think of.

Bram Stoker

Bram Stoker, author of the chilling story, *Dracula*, was born in Clontarf, Dublin in 1847. Bram, short for Abraham, was ill for a long time as a child and his mother used to tell him stories to cheer him up. It is said that she particularly enjoyed gruesome stories and she evidently passed on this interest to her son.

Stoker studied for a number of years at Trinity College, Dublin, and while there he showed a keen interest in drama and sport. After leaving university, he took up a job with the Civil Service in Dublin Castle. His main interest, however, was in theatre and writing. He wrote a drama column for a Dublin newspaper in the 1870s. In 1878, Stoker left Dublin for London where he became secretary to his great acting idol, Henry Irving. He managed Irving's theatre, The Lyceum.

Dracula

While in London, Stoker continued with his writing. He wrote about 18 books in all, but his name will be forever linked to his most famous book, *Dracula*, which was published in 1897. The book is a horror masterpiece which tells the story of the ghoulish Count Dracula, a Transylvanian vampire, who feeds nightly on the blood of humans. There has been much speculation as to where Stoker got the inspiration for his eerie tale. It is thought that he may have got the idea from reading about a bloodthirsty Romanian who lived in the 1400s. His name was Vlad Dracul!

Bram Stoker died in London in 1912, but his memory is very much alive today. His great novel has been translated into many languages and has inspired over 1,000 films, plays and books, as well as Ireland's first Gothic Art exhibition, which was held in Dublin Castle in 1999. The Bram Stoker International Summer School has been held annually in his native Clontarf since 1990. The summer school celebrates his life and works.

How to handle a vampire

The fictional Count Dracula inspired terror in people and left a trail of blood and destruction in his wake. But there are ways of dealing with vampires. Keeping garlic in a room is one way of warding off a vampire and making the sign of the cross is sure to send a vampire scurrying away. But if you really want to end the reign of a vampire, plunging a wooden stake into its heart is what's needed.

Still not sure whether you're dealing with a vampire or not? Get your suspect to look in the mirror and if he or she has no reflection, you know you've got the real thing! Reach for your garlic and your stake!

Mary Shelley

Mary Shelley was born in London in 1797. Both her parents were writers and from an early age Mary mixed with her parents' literary friends. When she was 16 years old, she ran away to France with the poet, Percy Bysshe Shelley, and married him two years later. Mary had four children, but three of them died very young. The death of her first child affected Mary deeply, and it is thought this may have shaped her first and greatest book, *Frankenstein*.

Frankenstein

This tells the story of Victor Frankenstein, a medical student, who used various parts taken from dead bodies to create a living creature. Mary first got the idea for the book while staying as a guest of the poet, Lord Byron, at Lake Geneva in Switzerland. During her stay, Byron challenged each of his guests to write a ghost story and *Frankenstein* was the result.

After her husband's death in 1822, Mary Shelley returned to England. She continued to write, publishing five more novels, as well as books on biography and travel. She also edited some of her husband's poems. None of her later works, however, were as successful as her great horror story, *Frankenstein*.

1. Many cultures have stories about monsters (think of the Cyclops, the Abominable Snowman, the Minotaur, the Kelpie). Choose one and find out what you can about it.

1. Examine the layout of this extract. How does it differ from others in this book?
2. Examine the artwork and read the chapter titles. What do you think the extract will be about?

Cloud Busting

Malorie Blackman

Chapter one: Mr Mackie Said

Mr Mackie said,
'Write a poem
About
Someone near to you,
Dear to you.
A pet,
A family member,
A friend.'
Funny, I thought,
How pets come first.
'That's your homework,'
Said Mr Mackie.
And the whole class groaned.
Except me.
'But poems are hard, sir!'
'Poems are boring!'
'Poems are for old people.'
'Poems are for boring, old people.'
'No one reads poetry –
Unless their teacher makes them.'
'No one likes poetry except
Poets –
Or those who don't have a life.'
And Mr Mackie said,
'ENOUGH!'

What would you have said?

And we all went quiet
'Cause Mr Mackie sure can shout.
Then Mr Mackie said,
'Hands up those who like rap music.'
And me and some others
Put our hands up.
'Hands up those who like pop music.'
And me and most others
Put our hands up.
'Hands up those who like classical
music.'
And me and almost everyone
Kept our hands down.
Except for Oliver.
Only Oliver
Put his hand up.
But then he would. ✦
And Mr Mackie said,
'Rap music and pop
And punk and rock
Have words.
And the words are poetry
Set to music,
That's all.'
'What about classical music?'
Asked Oliver.
But then he would.
'Classical music creates poetry
In your mind.
And your heart.
And your soul.
Even if there are no words
Being sung or spoken,
It still creates poetry
Inside you.'

And we all went quiet
Thinking.
Thinking.
And the strange thing is
No one laughed. ✦
Mr Mackie smiled.
'Any questions?'
Hands shot up.
'Does it have to rhyme, sir?'
'No.'
'How do we start, sir?'
'With whatever comes
Into your head.
Just let it out.
Don't hold back.
Don't stop yourselves.
Don't censor yourselves.
Let your words flow
Like a mountain stream
Like a babbling brook
Like a raging river
Like a tidal wave
A tsunami!
Like a cosmic wave,
Moving between galaxies.
Like a... like a...'
And we all groaned
'Cause Mr Mackie was off
Like a racehorse
Running its own race.
Just running 'cause it can,
Running to hear its hooves
Pound the ground.
Just running, running

✦ What does the boy mean by this?

✦ Why did no one laugh, do you think?

For love and pleasure ⭐
'Sir, can I write about
My dog?
My cat?
My goldfish?'
'Yes.'
'Sir, can I write about
My computer?
My skateboard?
Jaws, my teddy bear?'
'No.'
I put my hand up.
'Sir, can I write about Davey?'
The class went very still...
Very quiet. ⭐
My face began to burn
Burn hot then
Burn cold.
'Yes, Sam, you do that,'
Said Mr Mackie after the longest
  pause.
'Write about Dave.'
'What d'you want to write
About him for?'
That was Alex,
Talking at me.
Frowning at me.
Davey made him nervous,
Uncomfortable.
Uneasy.
Because of what he did.
Even though Davey isn't

Here any more
He still has the power
To make people
Uncomfortable,
Uneasy,
... to remember.
I didn't answer
My ex-best friend Alex.
What could I say?
I want to write about Davey
Because Mum says
You don't miss the water
Till the well runs dry. ⭐
I want to write about Davey
Because when he was here
I never gave him a second thought.
I want to write about Davey
Because now he's gone
I can't get him out of my head.
And I never thought I would,
But I miss him. ⭐
There!
I admit it.
He's gone.
And it's *his* fault –
The fault of the class idiot
The class bully.
And I miss him.
Not the class idiot.
He's gone too and
I don't miss him one bit.
I miss Davey.

⭐ Mr Mackie is compared to a racehorse. Is that a good comparison? Why?

⭐ Why do you think the class went quiet?

⭐ What does this saying mean? What does it mean here?

⭐ Why do you think Davey left?

His name was Davey.
Dave.
David Youngson.
But everyone called him Fizzy Feet.

Chapter two: What's in a name?

What's in a name? Not much.
That's what the class idiot said
After Davey's name
Was changed to Fizzy Feet.

It happened in assembly –
The second or third morning
After the long summer break,
About seven or eight months ago.

Maybe less, maybe more.
It was a long time ago,
But memories are longer.
Davey sat in front of me.

His light-brown hair
Wasn't long enough

To hide the frayed collar
Of his shirt.
His navy-blue school jumper
Had a small hole
At the elbow.
I shook my head and turned away.

My mum would never
Let me leave home
With holes at my
Elbows. No Way!

Davey was the new boy,
Full of uncertain smiles
And anxious eyes
And not much else.
My best friend Alex
Sat next to me
On my right
Playing with his Gameboy.

And on my left
Alicia. A-lic-i-a!
A name like April showers
Dropping gently onto spring flowers.

(Not that I'll leave in
The bit about Alicia
When I hand this poem
To Mr Mackie. No way!)

Mrs Spencer, the head,
Was droning on
And on

And on...

I was sleeping
With my eyes open
When it happened.
Waking us all up.

Davey jumped up,
Fell sideways
And started rubbing his legs
Saying 'Fizzy feet! I've got fizzy feet!'

We didn't have a clue
What he was talking about.
Mr Mackie ran over
To sort him out.

'Dave, what's the matter?
What's wrong?
What's going on?'
Mr Mackie was all concern.

'Fizzy feet!
I've got fizzy feet!'
Davey pulled off his shoes
And rubbed his toes. (What a pong!)

'What're you talking about?'
Mr Mackie began to frown.
'D'you mean you've got
Pins and needles?'

'Ow! Yes, that's what I said, sir!
Fizzy feet!'

What opinion is Sam forming of Davey and his family?

What do you think was wrong with Davey?

72

A moment's stunned silence.
Then we all roared like we had toothache.

Mr Mackie ranted
Mr Mackie raved
Mr Mackie was not happy
As he escorted Davey from the hall.

Fizzy Feet,
Dizzy, fizzy feet
Busy, dizzy, fizzy feet
What a dork!

Davey never lived that down.
The class bully
Wouldn't let him.
What a dork.

Davey hated the name
Fizzy Feet
But what could he do about it?
Not much. Nothing.
The class bully wouldn't let him.

*Chapter three: Facing The Truth –
With Haikus*

Mr Mackie said,
'Today, you lucky people,
We're doing haikus!'

'What's one of them, sir?'
'Poems to stir the senses,

Plus, they're very short.

A mere three lines long
Just seventeen syllables
Simple, pimple – right?

Three lines made up of
Words which are five syllables
Then seven, then five.'

'Haikus,' Alex groaned.
'What a waste of time and space.'
I didn't think so.

'Japanese poems.
Haikus...' sighed Mr Mackie.
'A pure, paced rhythm.'

'But sir,' said Alex,
'Haikus mean lots of counting.
That's not fair! That's maths!'

'Haikus are art, child.
Full of heart, soul and passion
So let your mind soar.'

'To where? And what for?'
'To the stars and beyond, child.'
'And when I land, sir?'

Mr Mackie frowned
Scratched his head and frowned some
more.

What is your impression of Davey?

Why did noboby stand up for Davey, do you think?

'You'll have memories.'

'Big deal!' Alex scoffed.
And that was the end of that.
Haikus bit the dust.

Haiku for Davey:

We should've been friends
But the bad thing that happened
To you changed my life.

Why do you think haikus 'bit the dust'?

1. How did Davey get his nickname?
2. What is a haiku?
3. How do we know that Sam was bored at assembly?

4. What advice does Mr Mackie give to the class when they ask about how to get started writing poetry?
5. How does Mr Mackie explain what a haiku is? Would you agree with him? Why?
6. How does Alex disrupt the class? How does Mr Mackie react?
7. In very simple words the author creates some powerful images. What is your favourite image in this extract?
8. What kind of teacher is Mr Mackie? Find evidence from the text to back up your opinion.

9. What kind of person is Sam? Explain why you think this.
10. Why did the class bully pick on Davey do you think?
11. Do you want to find out what happened to Davey? How does the author make you want to read on?

12. Create a haiku of your own.
13. Bullying is a very serious offence. What can you do if it happens to you? Or if you see it happening to somebody else?

CLOUD BUSTING

MALORIE BLACKMAN

Play the game

Play the lighting up game. You will need:
- dice
- counters

The first lamps were made about 50 000 years ago using hollowed-out stones filled with animal fat. In some countries large seashells were used instead of hollow stones.

Candles were first used over 2000 years ago. They were made from beeswax or from **tallow**. The Dublin firm, Rathbornes, has been making candles for over 500 years.

Lighting up time

You fall asleep, fire goes out. Go back to the start.

Firelight frighten wolves. Have ar extra go.

You run out of animal fat. Return to no.2

You are able to see for longer now. Go exploring 2 places to no.12

Bee have m lots mor wax thi year, go on to no.1

76

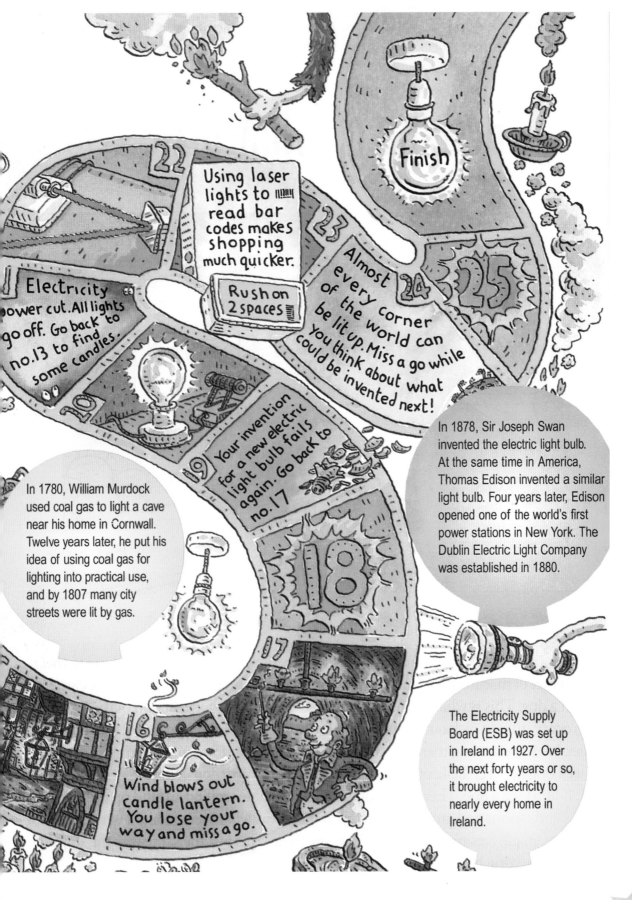

Finish

Using laser lights to read bar codes makes shopping much quicker.

Rush on 2 spaces

Almost every corner of the world can be lit up. Miss a go while you think about what could be invented next!

Electricity power cut. All lights go off. Go back to no.13 to find some candles.

Your invention for a new electric light bulb fails again. Go back to no.17

In 1878, Sir Joseph Swan invented the electric light bulb. At the same time in America, Thomas Edison invented a similar light bulb. Four years later, Edison opened one of the world's first power stations in New York. The Dublin Electric Light Company was established in 1880.

In 1780, William Murdock used coal gas to light a cave near his home in Cornwall. Twelve years later, he put his idea of using coal gas for lighting into practical use, and by 1807 many city streets were lit by gas.

The Electricity Supply Board (ESB) was set up in Ireland in 1927. Over the next forty years or so, it brought electricity to nearly every home in Ireland.

Wind blows out candle lantern. You lose your way and miss a go.

1. Read the first sentence. What do you learn about the girl telling the story?
2. The character has an interesting name. What images does it bring to your mind?
3. Who or what is Winn-Dixie do you think?

Because of Winn-Dixie

Kate DiCamillo

Chapter one

My name is India Opal Buloni, and last summer my daddy, the preacher, sent me to the store for a box of macaroni-and-cheese, some white rice and two tomatoes, and I came back with a dog. This is what happened: I walked into the produce section of the Winn-Dixie grocery store to pick out my two tomatoes and I almost bumped right into the store manager. He was standing there all red-faced, screaming and waving his arms around. 'Who let a dog in here?' he kept on shouting. 'Who let a dirty dog in here?'

At first, I didn't see a dog. There were just a lot of vegetables rolling around on the floor, tomatoes and onions and green peppers. And there was what seemed like a whole army of Winn-Dixie employees running around waving their arms just the same way the store manager was waving his.

And then the dog came running around the corner. He was a big dog. And ugly. And he looked like he was having a real good time. His tongue was hanging out and he was wagging his tail. He skidded to a stop and smiled right at me. I had never before in my life seen a dog smile, but that is what he did. He pulled back his lips and showed me all his teeth. Then he wagged his tail so hard that he knocked some oranges off a display and they went rolling everywhere, mixing in with the tomatoes and onions and green peppers. ⭐

The manager screamed, 'Somebody grab that dog!'

The dog went running over to the manager, wagging his tail and smiling. He stood up on his hind legs. You could tell that all he wanted to do was get face to face with the manager and thank him for the good time he was having in the produce department, but somehow he ended up knocking the manager over. And the manager must have been having a bad day because, lying there on the floor, right in front of everybody, he started to cry. The dog leaned over him, real concerned, and licked his face.

'Please,' said the manager, 'somebody call the pound.'

'Wait a minute!' I hollered. 'That's my dog. Don't call the pound.'

All the Winn-Dixie employees turned around and looked at me, and I knew I had done something big. And maybe stupid, too. But I couldn't help it. I couldn't let that dog go to the pound.

'Here, boy,' I said.

The dog stopped licking the manager's face and put his ears up in the air and looked at me, like he was trying to remember where he knew me from.

'Here, boy,' I said again. And then I figured that the dog was probably just like everybody else in the world, that he would want to get called by a name, only I didn't know what his name was, so I just said the first thing that came into my head. I said, 'Here, Winn-Dixie.'

And that dog came trotting over to me just like he had been doing it his whole life.

The manager sat up and gave me a hard stare, like maybe I was making fun of him.

'It's his name,' I said. 'Honest.'

The manager said, 'Don't you know not to bring a dog into a grocery store?'

'Yes sir,' I told him. 'He got in by mistake.

⭐ How does the dog endear himself to Opal?

I'm sorry. It won't happen again.'

'Come on, Winn-Dixie,' I said to the dog.

I started walking and he followed along behind me as I went out of the produce department and down the cereal aisle and past all the cashiers and out the door. Once we were safe outside, I checked him over real careful and he didn't look that good. He was big, but skinny; you could see his ribs. And there were bald patches all over him, places where he didn't have any fur at all. Mostly, he looked like a big piece of old brown carpet that had been left out in the rain.

'You're a mess,' I told him. 'I bet you don't belong to anybody.'

He smiled at me. He did that thing again, where he pulled back his lips and showed me his teeth. He smiled so big that it made him sneeze. It was like he was saying, 'I know I'm a mess. Isn't it funny?

It's hard not to immediately fall in love with a dog who has a good sense of humour.

'Come on,' I told him. 'Let's see what the preacher has to say about you.'

And the two of us, me and Winn-Dixie, started walking home.

Chapter two

That summer I found Winn-Dixie was also the summer me and the preacher moved to Naomi, Florida, so he could be the new preacher at the Open Arms Baptist Church of Naomi. My daddy is a good preacher and a nice man, but sometimes it's hard for me to think about him as my daddy because he spends so much time preaching or thinking about preaching or getting ready to preach. And so, in my mind, I think of him as 'the preacher'. Before I was born he was a missionary in India and that is how I got my first name. But he calls me by my second name, Opal, because that was his mother's name. And he loved her a lot.

Anyway, while me and Winn-Dixie walked home, I told him how I got my name and I told him how I had just moved to Naomi. I also told him about the preacher and how he was a good man, even if he was too distracted with sermons and prayers and suffering people to go grocery shopping.

'But you know what?' I told Winn-Dixie, 'you are a suffering dog, so maybe he will take to you right away. Maybe he'll let me keep you.'

Winn-Dixie looked up at me and wagged his tail. He was kind of limping like something was wrong with one of his legs. And I have to admit, he stank. Bad. He was

⭐ What are your impression of Opal so far?

⭐ Why do you think Opal was so keen to keep the dog?

an ugly dog, but already I loved him with all my heart.

When we got to the Friendly Corners Trailer Park, I told Winn-Dixie that he had to behave right and be quiet, because this was an all-adult trailer park and the only reason I got to live in it was because the preacher was a preacher and I was a good, quiet kid. I was what the Friendly Corners Trailer Park manager, Mr Alfred, called 'an exception'. ⭐

And I told Winn-Dixie he had to act like an exception, too; specifically, I told him not to pick any fights with Mr Alfred's cats or Mrs Detweller's little yappy Yorkie dog, Samuel. Winn-Dixie looked up at me while I was telling him everything, and I swear he understood.

'Sit', I told him when we got to my trailer. He sat right down. He had good manners. 'Stay here', I told him. 'I'll be right back.'

The preacher was sitting in the living room, working at the little fold-out table. He had papers spread all around him and he was rubbing his nose, which always meant he was thinking. Hard.

'Daddy?' I said.

'Hmmm', he said back.

⭐ What does Opal mean by this?

'Daddy, do you know how you always tell me that we should help those less fortunate than ourselves?'

'Hmmm-hmmm,' he said. He rubbed his nose and looked around at his papers.

'Well,' I said, 'I found a Less Fortunate at the grocery store.'

'Is that right?' he said.

'Yes sir,' I told him. I stared at the preacher really hard. Sometimes he reminded me of a turtle hiding inside its shell, in there thinking about things and not ever sticking his head out into the world.  'Daddy, I was wondering. Could this Less Fortunate, could he stay with us for a while?'

Finally the preacher looked up at me. 'Opal,' he said, 'what are you talking about?'

'I found a dog,' I told him. 'And I want to keep him.'

'No dogs,' the preacher said. 'We've talked about this before. You don't need a dog.'

'I know it.' I said. 'I know I don't need a dog. But this dog needs me. Look,' I said. I went to the trailer door and I hollered, 'Winn-Dixie!'

Winn-Dixie's ears shot up in the air and he grinned and sneezed, and then he came limping up the steps and into the trailer and put his head right in the preacher's lap, right on top of a pile of papers.

The preacher looked at Winn-Dixie. He looked at his ribs and his matted-up fur and the places where he was bald. The preacher's nose wrinkled up. Like I said, the dog smelled pretty bad.

Do you think this is a good description of the preacher?

Winn-Dixie looked up at the preacher. He pulled back his lips and showed the preacher all of his crooked yellow teeth and wagged his tail and knocked some of the preacher's papers off the table. Then he sneezed and some more papers fluttered to the floor.

'What did you call this dog?' the preacher asked.

'Winn-Dixie,' I whispered. I was afraid to say anything too loud. I could see that Winn-Dixie was having a good effect on the preacher. He was making him poke his head out of his shell.

'Well,' said the preacher, 'he's a stray if ever I've seen one.' He put down his pencil and scratched Winn-Dixie behind the ears. 'And a Less Fortunate, too. That's for sure. Are you looking for a home?' the preacher asked, real soft, to Winn-Dixie.

Winn-Dixie wagged his tail.

'Well,' the preacher said, 'I guess you've found one.'

> What tactics did Opal use to persuade her father to keep Winn-Dixie?

1. How did the character get her name?
2. Why does Opal call the dog Winn-Dixie?
3. Why was Opal allowed to live in the all-adult trailer park?

4. What kind of relationship does Opal have with her father?
5. Find examples of American language. What words would we use instead? Think of other American expressions.

6. The author of this book seems to delight in unusual names. Find some examples and say what they make you think about.
7. What kind of character is Opal do you think?
8. What do you imagine life is like for Opal?
9. There is lots of humour in this extract. Which is your favourite example?
10. There is no mention of Opal's mother in this extract. How is her absence felt?

11. Describe another story which shows a strong connection between the main character and an animal.
12. Opal said: '… and I knew I had done something big. And maybe stupid too.' Have you ever thought like this? Talk about it.

Because of Winn-Dixie
Kate DiCamillo

1. Read the title of the chapter and look at the illustration. What do you predict this story will be about?
2. This story is set during the famine in Ireland. What do you know about the famine?

Under the Hawthorn Tree

Marita Conlon-McKenna

Chapter one: Hunger

The air felt cold and damp as Eily stirred in her bed and tried to pull a bit more of the blanket up to her shoulders. Her little sister Peggy moved against her. Peggy was snoring again. She always did when she had a cold.

The fire was nearly out. The hot ash made a soft glow in the gloom of the cottage. Mother was crooning quietly to the baby. Bridget's eyes were closed and her soft face looked paler than ever as she lay wrapped in Mother's shawl, her little fist clinging to a piece of the long chestnut-coloured hair.

Bridget was ill – they all knew it. Underneath the wrapped shawl her body was too thin, her skin white and either too hot or too cold to the touch. Mother held her all day and all night as if trying to will some of her strength into the little one so loved.

Eily could feel tears at the back of her eyes. Sometimes she thought that maybe this was all a dream and soon she would wake up and laugh at it, but the hunger pain in her tummy and the sadness in her heart were enough to know that it was real. She closed her eyes and remembered. ⭐

⭐ What evidence do we have that this family is in trouble?

It was hard to believe that it was only a little over a year ago, and they sitting in the old school room, when Tim O'Kelly had run in to get his brother John and told them all to 'Make a run home quick to help with lifting the spuds as a pestilence had fallen on the place and they were rotting in the ground.'

They all waited for the master to get his stick and shout at Tim: Away out of it, you fool, to disturb the learning, but were surprised when he shut his book and told them to make haste and 'Mind, no dawdling,' and 'Away home to give a hand.' They all ran so fast that their breath caught in their throats, half afraid of what they would find at home.

Eily remembered. Father was sitting on the stone wall, his head in his hands. Mother was kneeling in the field, her hands and apron covered in mud as she pulled the potatoes from the ground, and all around the air heavy with a smell – that smell, rotting, horrible, up your nose, in your mouth. The smell of badness and disease. Across the valley the men cursed and the women prayed to God to save them. Field after field of potatoes had died and rotted in the ground. The crop, their food-crop was gone. All the children stared – eyes large and frightened, for even they knew that now the hunger would come.

Eily snuggled up against Peggy's back and soon felt warmer. She was drowsy and finally drifted back to sleep. ⭐

'Eily! Eily! Are you getting up?' whispered Peggy.

The girls began to stretch and after a while they threw off the blankets. Eily went over to the fire and put a sod of turf on the embers. The basket was nearly empty. That was a job for Michael.

Both girls went outside. The early morning sun was shining. The grass was damp with dew. They didn't delay as it was chilly in their shifts. Back in the cottage, Mother was still asleep and little Bridget dozed against her.

'Is there something to eat?'

'Oh, Michael, easy known you're up,' jeered Eily.

'Go on, Eily, look, have a look,' he pleaded.

'Away outside with you and wash that grime off your face and we'll see then.'

The sunlight peered in through the open cottage door. The place is dusty and dirty, thought Eily.

The baby coughed and woke. Eily took her and sat in the fireside chair as Mother busied herself. There were three greyish leftover spuds. Mother sliced them and poured out a drink of skimmed milk from the large jug. It was little enough. No one spoke.

⭐ What kind of atmosphere has the author created so far?

They ate in silence, each with their own thoughts.

Michael began to talk... to ask for... but changed his mind. Time had taught him a lesson. The first few times he had asked for more, his father or mother had lifted the wooden spoon and brought it down on the palm of his hand. Later, his pleas had been met by a sadness in his father's eyes and his mother bursting into tears. This he could not take on top of the pinches and squeezing of his two sisters. Things were better left unsaid.

By midday the situation had improved. There was heat in the sun and a warm breeze blowing. Michael went up the road to his friend Pat and together they would walk the mile to the bog to see if they could get a fill for the basket.

Bridget's breathing was rattly, but she slept. Mother, encouraged, took the shifts and a few dirty clothes to wash and then spread them outside to dry. She shook the blankets and laid them across the stone wall.

Peggy's long brown hair was unplaited. It hung lank and greasy. Mother bent her over as she poured water from the bucket on the hair and scrubbed at her scalp. The cries from Peggy were nothing to what followed when Mother produced the fine comb and began to pull it through the length and tangles, peering each time to see if any lice or nits were in it. Eily laughed, knowing that since she had had her turn only two weeks before, she would escape today.

Later, Mother despatched the two of them up the lane to Mary Kate Conway for a bit of goose grease – if she had it – to rub on Bridget's chest. Mary Kate had a gift for healing and always helped those who were sick or in trouble.

Her cottage was surrounded by a thick hedge in order to provide a bit of privacy for those who needed to visit her.

The old lady was sitting on a stool outside in the sunshine.

'Well, if it isn't the two best little girls in the world,' joked Mary Kate. 'What can I do for you, pets?'

'Mother needs some goose grease for the baby,' pleaded Eily.

'The poor, poor child,' murmured Mary Kate. 'What a time to come into the world.'

She got up from her stool and beckoned to the girls to follow her. Peggy lagged behind, clutching at Eily's dress. She had heard stories about the old lady and was a bit afraid of her.

The cottage was dark and smelly. Mary Kate hobbled over to the old wooden dresser. It was filled with jars and bottles. She mumbled to herself as she lifted down different jars and opened the lids to peep at the contents. Finally, sniffing what she wanted, she handed it down to Eily.

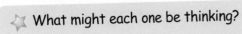

What might each one be thinking?

What did Mary Kate mean by this?

'Mind you tell your mother I want my jar back when she is finished.'

'Will it make Bridget better?' Eily was amazed at the bravery of little seven-year-old Peggy's question.

Mary Kate frowned. 'I don't know, pet. There is so much sickness at the moment – strange sickness – I do my best.'

With that, Mary Kate began to head back out towards the sunlight. Just outside the door she put her hand into the pocket of her apron and produced an apple. A dirty old apple. She gave it a polish. The girls tried not to look, but with a flourish she handed it to Peggy.

Peggy's eyes were round and wide. Eily blinked.

'Many thanks... we couldn't take it from you... thank you, but it wouldn't be fair,' Eily began.

'As green and hard as the hobs in hell,' laughed Mary Kate, throwing back her head to display her toothless gums. 'Shure, I can't eat it.' ☆

The girls smiled and Peggy carried the apple like a precious jewel safely home to be shared by all.

That night they had the yellow meal cooked with some melted lard and a few wild spring onions Mother had found to hide the flavour. The apple was quartered and

☆ What are your impressions of Mary Kate?

savoured, though there was no denying its crisp hardness and sharp taste.

'It is two weeks since your father went to work on the roads, and still no word from him,' began Mother. Eily knew her mother was worried, between Bridget's illness and the sack of the old yellow meal in the corner getting smaller and smaller by the day.

'I don't know what we'll all come to or how we'll manage,' Mother continued, shaking her head.

'There is even talk of the big house being closed up and the master and his family moving back to England for good.'

Michael, sensing the near despair in her voice piped up: 'I've got some good news. Listen, Ma, just listen.'

Sometimes it was hard to believe that he was only a boy of nine, with his thick black curly hair like his father and the soft kind blue eyes of his mother. He hated to see her sad.

'Pat and I were up on the bog – we went a bit further than usual and we found a part that isn't all cut away yet. Pat's father is going up there tomorrow with him and will cut it and lay it and he says if this wind and drying continues we can have some for our place once we collect it and carry it ourselves. Isn't that grand?'

Mother smiled. 'Dan Collins is a good man, there's no doubt.'

She settled herself into the chair and relaxed a bit. Eily knelt down near her and Peggy sat in her lap.

'Tell us about when you were a girl – go on, please,' they all begged. ⭐

'Are ye not all fed up with my old stories,' she chided.

'Never,' assured Michael.

Well, then,' she began. 'Mary Ellen, that was my mother and your grandmother, what Eily's called after, lived with her two sisters Nano and Lena...'

There was nothing like a story before bedtime.

⭐ **Why did the children beg for a story do you think?**

1. What word does the author use to describe the disease that attacked the potatoes?
2. What gift had Mary Kate Conway?
3. How did Mary Kate describe the apple she gave to the girls?

4. What did we learn about a.) Eily and b.) Michael during this extract? Back up your answer with some examples.
5. Skim through the extract. Describe the food the children ate.
6. Mother had many worries. List some of them.

7. Some characters play small but important roles in a story. Find such a character in this extract and say what role he/she plays.
8. What is the mood of this story? How did the author create this mood?
9. The children took on many responsibilities in this extract. Why was this?
10. How do you think the father felt having to leave his family? Do you think they will meet up again?

11. If you had been alive during the Famine in Ireland, how do you think you would have coped?
12. If the potato crop failed today, how do you think it would affect people in Ireland?

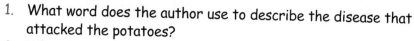

1. Look through the extract. How is it different from other extracts in the book?
2. Which is your favourite illustration? Why?
3. What do you think will happen in the extract?

The Long March

Marie-Louise Fitzpatrick

It is 1847, and Choona, a young Choctaw and his two sisters, Talowa and Hoshonti, are gathered together with the rest of the tribe. They have been called to a meeting to learn of a terrible famine happening in a faraway country, Ireland, at that time.

Talowa, Hoshonti, and I were proud to have a great-grandmother. Few of our friends even had grandparents. Great-Grandmother was the oldest person in our tribe. She was called Talihoyo, Rockwoman. When she was young an enemy tribe's warriors had sneaked across the river into the cornfields where she and the other women were working. Instead of screaming and running away, she encouraged the women to stand their ground and throw rocks at the warriors until they turned and fled back across the river. Great-Grandmother was much respected and everyone greeted her as she sat down.

Soon the circle was packed and noisy. Moshi stepped forward and asked for quiet. My uncle was the Minkoapilachi, the ceremonial speaker for the tribal leaders. He gave the formal welcome to bring the people together in council. Then he began to tell the tribe the story he and Father had heard the day before.

He spoke of a country far away where the people ate potatoes. Now the potatoes were rotting in the ground. There was nothing else to eat and the people were sick and starving. Whole villages of people were leaving their homes and walking the land in search of food. They were eating the leaves from the trees and the grass from the ground in a desperate attempt to stay alive. They were dying as they walked. The mouths of the dead were stained green. ⭐

Moshi said the Memphis Committee had brought the story to the tribal leaders from Washington, DC, where a big meeting had been held to see what could be done to help these Irish people.

'We too are being asked to help them,' said Moshi.

Moshi waited to see what people would say to this, but no one spoke.

'We are being asked to help them,' repeated Moshi.

Still there was silence, and then a man called Mishima Abi spoke. He was a respected warrior and had taken enemy lives in battle. He spoke forcefully.

'These people are Nahullo, Europeans,' he said.

'The Nahullo have come to our land and taken it from us. They have caused our people to die. It is because of them that the bones of our people lie scattered along the trail of the Long March. The Nahullo only take, they do not give. Why should we help them?'

Some people murmured in agreement.

Mishima Abi lifted his hands in appeal.

'Why should we help the Nahullo? Why? Why?'

Tension filled the circle.

The war words had been effective.

The silence stretched out.

Then Great-Grandmother cleared her throat to speak. Immediately everyone turned to hear what Talihoyo would say. She had the attention of the whole council. Even the children crept forward from the shadows. Her words would carry weight. She was our oldest elder. ⭐

'Long ago,' she began, 'when the world was young, the ground split open and the Choctaw people walked out of the earth into the living land…'

I thought my great-grandmother had gotten off the point, but I didn't care. I loved her stories. I slid down to the floor beside my sisters.

'. . . the ground closed behind the people,' continued Talihoyo, 'and they called the mount where the earth had opened Nanih Waiyha and said they would live only around her, their mother. They believed that if they left her, they would be lost forever.

⭐ Describe the atmosphere created by the author.

⭐ What do you think she will say?

Our people lived well from the earth, taking what they needed and leaving what they did not. They farmed the land. Hunted in the forests, and fished the rivers. Their warriors were respected by enemy tribes, and they defended Choctaw villages fiercely.'  Talihoyo glanced toward Mishima Abi and smiled.

'Then the Nahullo came – the Spanish, the French, the English. They were different. Their skins were white. Their ways were strange. Their weapons were powerful. At first the Choctaw welcomed these people. They knew they must learn to live with them, and so our people gave these newcomers land, thinking there was enough for all. In return they got guns and horses and many things they had not seen before. For more than one hundred winters the different people lived side by side, but always the strangers wanted land, more land. In the end they wanted it all, and our people could do nothing to stop them.

'Sixteen winters ago at Dancing Rabbit Creek, the last of our lands in Mississippi were signed away. We were to break our promise to the Creator and leave Nanih Waiyha and the land of our ancestors.'

Talihoyo was silent for a moment. I glanced around the circle. Everyone was quiet. I thought I saw dread in many eyes.

'We packed our belongings, those we could carry,' said the old woman, 'and we prepared to leave our homeland. We left behind our villages, our great fields of corn, our hunting grounds, the ancient burial places of our people. As we left, we kissed the

⭐ **What does this tell you about the Choctaws' relationship with the land?**

ground and hugged the trees. The women clung to the bushes that overhung the Mississippi River.

'It was winter when the march began, thousands of us stretching to the horizon like a great herd of buffalo. It was cold. The rivers were freezing, the walking was hard. Soon the food was running out. The soldiers who marched us west to the New Lands could not explain why the blankets and food the government promised did not come.

'Every night we lay down to sleep on frozen ground, and every morning there were those who did not wake. People, began to starve. Children became sick. The fever came and old and young slipped away from us into the spirit world. The ground became too hard to dig, and we could not bury our dead. We stripped their bodies and, as our ancestors once did, lifted them into the forks of the trees. In this way we buried them in the sky.

'The march went on, day after day, 500 miles of swamp, river, forest, mountain, snow, ice. Five hundred miles of death. Now we walked alone, though together, each of us trying to stay alive. Trying to finish the day's journey. Waking each morning to walk again. Thousands of us walking in silence. Families fell behind to nurse the dying, to wait and watch with them, to leave their bodies behind, then to join the long march again – on and on, walking bones.

'Mountain Fork was the last river to cross. Our journey was over, they told us. Half our people were gone – All the old ones.

All the small children.

Gone.

Our journey was over, they told us. Yet we have walked in circles ever since. We have plowed new fields, but the land is foreign to us. We have built new homes, yet we are lost, just as our ancestors said we would be.

'I am old, without teeth,' said Talihoyo. 'I am half-blind, but when I close my eyes the faces of the dead come to me through the blackness. We have walked the trail of tears.

How do you feel listening to Talihoyo's story?

Why are they lost do you think?

The Irish people walk it now. We can help them as we could not help ourselves. Our help will be like an arrow shot through time. It will land many winters from now to wait as a blessing for our unborn generations.'

Talihoyo was silent then. No one spoke, and I could see that the men and women were far away. I looked at my mother. Her gaze seemed to go right through me, as if I wasn't there. I dropped my eyes. After a while my father stood up. He addressed the council.

'We have only a little, but let us gather what we have and send it to Ireland.'

The journey home was a quiet one. My sisters and I did not dare to break the silence.

Notes

The Choctaw Nation: They were hunters and farmers who originally lived in the Southeastern region of the US (Mississippi, Alabama, Louisiana). In 1786, the United States government recognised the Choctaw as an independent nation. Along with the Creek, Cherokee, Seminole, and the Chickasaw, they were sometimes known as the 'Five Civilized Tribes'. But all five 'civilized tribes' were still forced off their land in the 1830s. The journey west to 'Indian Territory' caused much death and suffering for these nations. Indian Territory, in turn, came under pressure from white settlers and eventually became the state of Oklahoma. Today there are 8,000 Choctaw in Mississippi, descendants of those who would not leave in 1831. Both Oklahoma and Mississippi Choctaw have their own constitutions, elect tribal councils and chiefs, and administer their own affairs.

The Irish Potato Famine (1845–1849): At this time, Ireland was governed by Britain. The majority of its eight million people lived on small patches of land rented from wealthy landlords. The potato is a nourishing vegetable that yields well even in poor soil, so the Irish had come to depend on it as their main food. A potato blight hit Europe in 1845 and destroyed most of that year's crop. In 1846 and 1847, there was a total crop failure. 1847 is known to the Irish as 'Black '47'. Over one million people died of starvation and famine-related diseases during these four years. Over one million people emigrated to other countries.

New Lands/Indian Territory: Lands to which the Southeastern tribes and others were removed between 1831 and 1839. In 1907, in violation of treaty agreements, this area became the state of Oklahoma. Okla Homa is Choctaw for 'Red People'.

Memphis Committee: On February 9, 1847, a huge public meeting was held in Washington DC under the chairmanship of the vice-president of the United States. The meeting discussed the Irish Potato Famine and recommended that meetings should be held in every city, town and village in order to raise funds. The Memphis Committee was a committee of the Society of Friends (Quakers). They brought the news of the Washington meeting to all the tribal leaders.

Choctaw names and words used in The Long March:

Moshi:	The name given to a mother's eldest brother. This uncle had a special relationship with, and responsibility for, his sister's sons.
Talowa:	'Song'
Hoshonti:	'Cloud'
Talihoyo:	'Rockwoman'. The story of Talihoyo is a Choctaw legend.
Mishima Abi:	'Over there he killed'.
Nanih Waiyha:	'Productive mountain'. The Choctaw creation mound in Winston County, Mississippi.

1. Why was Great-Grandmother called Rockwoman?
2. Why did Mishima Abi not want to help the Irish people?

3. There are some Native American words used in the extract. Find as many as you can and explain them.
4. Great-Grandmother was a powerful storyteller. Find evidence of this in the extract.
5. What do you learn about Choctaw culture from this extract?
6. In what ways did the Nahullo treat the Choctaws badly?

7 Do you think it was easy for Great-Grandmother to talk about the march? Why?
8. In what way did the long march change the Choctaw people forever?
9. How do you know that Great-Grandmother's story deeply affected those who listened?

10. Find out more about the Native Americans, their culture and way of life, and how the European settlers treated them.
11. How was the hardship suffered by Irish people like that suffered by the Choctaws? Do you think this affects how we respond to famine today?

Famine in Ireland

Landowners

During the Great Famine, or *Gorta Mór*, conditions in Ireland were very different from today. The majority of Irish people didn't own the land they worked and lived on. They had to pay rent to wealthy landlords for the use of the land. Some landlords lived in Ireland while others were 'absentee landlords', who lived in England.

Tenants

A small number of farmers had enough land to make a reasonable living. They could afford to keep a pig and some cows, they could grow enough food to feed their families and pay the rent. They lived in comfortable homes with outhouses for their animals.

However, many had only a tiny patch of land beside their cottages. They survived by working for better-off farmers. They lived in small mud cabins in constant fear of being evicted if they failed to pay the rent. Some had no land at all and depended on begging or seasonal farm work.

Population

From the early 1800s, the population began to increase greatly. People married at an earlier age and had larger families. It was difficult for young couples to afford a place of their own, so parents often shared the small amount of land they owned with their children. This meant that the same small patch of land had to feed more mouths.

Food

The potato was nutritious and easy to grow. It was planted in spring, harvested in autumn and stored in pits over the winter. Over the years, it became the sole source of food for the vast majority of Irish people, most of whom could not afford anything else to eat. Potatoes were eaten at every meal along with a drink of milk.

Potato blight struck the crop in 1845 and destroyed about a third of it. This was followed by total crop failures in 1846 and 1847. Other crops were not affected.

Even though hundreds of thousands were starving, food was still being exported from Ireland to other countries where people could afford to buy it.

A list of food exports from Cork on a single day, 14 November 1848, ran as follows:

- ✔ 147 bales of bacon
- ✔ 120 casks and 135 barrels of pork
- ✔ 5 casks of ham
- ✔ 149 casks miscellaneous provisions
- ✔ 1,996 sacks and 950 barrels of oats
- ✔ 300 bags of flour
- ✔ 300 head of cattle
- ✔ 239 sheep
- ✔ 9,398 firkins of butter
- ✔ 542 boxes of eggs

A soup kitchen

[extract from Robert Kee's *Ireland: A History* (Weidenfeld & Nicolson)]

Relief efforts

Cheap corn was imported to help the starving people, but many were too poor to buy it. In 1845, the English government also funded public relief works such as roads, walls and bridge building, to enable people to work to earn money, but these were withdrawn the following year. Many people were too weak to do such work and died on the roadside. With starvation came disease and thousands died. Some landlords did everything in their power to help their tenants but others did nothing and evicted their tenants when they could not pay their rent. Workhouses had been set up shortly before the Famine where those who had nothing could go for help. They were dreaded places where families were separated from each other once inside. Before long, the workhouses were full and couldn't cope with the demand. Soup-kitchens were also set up to try and help the poor. By 1847, three million people were dependent on soup-kitchens for food.

People were treated very harshly in the workhouse:

Name	Offence	Date	Punishment inflicted by master or other officer
Owen Trainer	Stealing Onions	1 July 1851	Flogged
Twenty-nine women	Neglecting and refusing to work	24 September 1851	Dinner and supper milk stopped
James Ackison	Going to Mass without permission	14 July 1852	Six hours in Lock-up
Samual McGuaire	Unruly conduct	14 July 1852	Flogged and three hours in Lock-up
John Byrnes	Poaching	1 December 1852	Flogged
Mary Carroll	Refusing to work and damaging her clothes	8 November 1854	Nine hours in Lock-up
Mary Carroll	Persistently refusing to work	9 November 1854	Seven hours in Lock-up

Extract from *Workhouse Offences and Punishment Book*

Emigration

Hundreds of thousands left the country between 1847 and 1851 and emigrated to England and America. The ships became known as 'coffin ships' because about 20% of passengers died. This was caused by overcrowding, disease and a lack of adequate food and water. When they arrived emigrants were put in quarantine because there were fears that they might bring typhoid into the country.

Annie Moore and her two younger brothers were the first people to pass through Ellis Island Emigration Station, New York, January 1st, 1892.

End of the Famine

The Famine finally ended in 1851. Ireland was a changed place. The population had decreased drastically, the Irish language was weakened and emigration became a feature of Irish life.

Examine the map:
1. Which counties saw the: a.) greatest fall in population; b.) least fall in population? Think of reasons for this.
2. Which areas witnessed a rise in population? Why do you think this occurred? How was your own area affected?

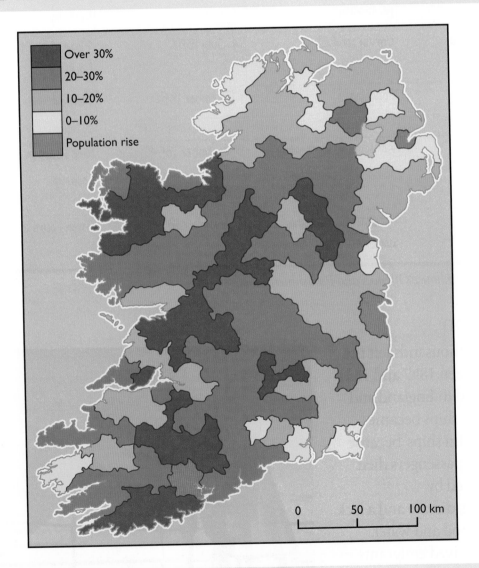

Legend:
Over 30%
20–30%
10–20%
0–10%
Population rise

0   50   100 km

1. What were the advantages and disadvantages of going into a workhouse?
2. Do you think the punishments in the workhouse were fair?
3. Which offence do you think was the most serious? Why?
4. Find out which countries Irish people have emigrated to.
5. What were 'coffin ships'?

Art at the National Gallery

Richard T. Moynan

Richard T. Moynan was an Irish portrait and figure painter of the nineteenth century. He excelled in portraying the lives of the poor and used the children of the streets as models.

This painting *Military Manoeuvres* below, shows Leixlip in Co Kildare, painted exactly as it was in 1891, apart from the church spire, which the artist added to make it more interesting.

This painting is important because it shows how people lived in the nineteenth century. Look closely at the painting to see how children dressed in Ireland over 100 years ago.

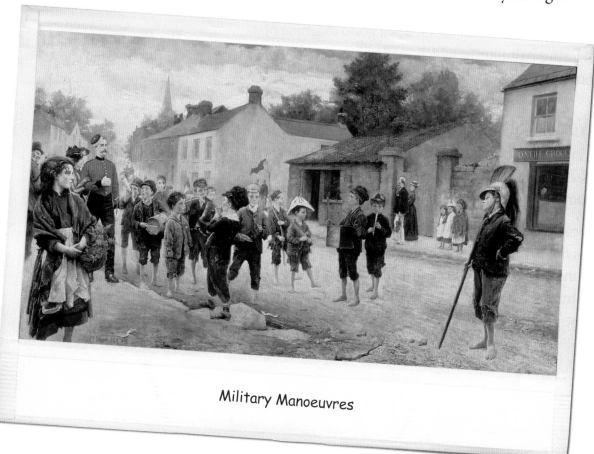

Military Manoeuvres

1. Pictures that tell stories are called narratives. In *Military Manoeuvres* the boys are pretending to be an army band. Can you see who they are making fun of?
2. Girls and older people have stopped to watch the fun. You can see the grocer looking out of his shop window. If you were to put speech bubbles on the painting above, what would each person say?
3. There are lots of musical instruments in this painting. Some of them are real and some are pretend. Name them.

Frederic Burton

This watercolour *The Meeting on the Turret Stairs* by Frederic Burton portrays a scene from a Danish ballad. The story describes the doomed relationship between Hellelil and her bodyguard Hildebrand, the Prince of Engellend.

Hellelil's father disapproved of the prince as a husband for his daughter and ordered his sons to kill him. Their tragic love results in the killing of seven of Hellelil's brothers by Hildebrand and his own death at the hand of the youngest brother.

The artist chose the moment of the couple's sad final meeting on the turret stairs. It is a good example of narrative painting, in which we feel for the doomed romantic couple.

The Meeting on the Turret Stairs

Wendy Shea

Wendy Shea has drawn an amusing version of *The Meeting on the Turret Stairs*, called *Eating on the Turret Stairs*.

Look closely at the two pictures. Note how the artist has made the transition from a serious drawing to a funny one. A cartoon is a simple drawing showing the features of its subjects in a humorous and exaggerated way.

Eating on the Turret Stairs

1. Look carefully at the two pictures.
   a.) How are they similar?
   b.) How are they different?
2. Think up names for the characters in Wendy Shea's picture?
3. What do you think is the story behind *Eating on the Turret Stairs*?
4. Choose a famous painting. Draw an amusing version of it.

A Slash of Blue

Emily Dickinson

A slash of Blue –
A sweep of Gray –
Some scarlet patches on the way,
Compose an Evening Sky –
A little purple – slipped between
Some Ruby Trousers hurried on –
A Wave of Gold –
A Bank of Day –
This just makes out the Morning Sky.

The Paint Box

E. V. Rieu

'Cobalt and umber and ultramarine,
Ivory black and emerald green –
What shall I paint to give pleasure to you?'
'Paint for me somebody utterly new.'

'I have painted you tigers in crimson and white.'
'The colours were good and you painted aright.'
'I have painted the cook and a camel in blue
And a panther in purple.' 'You painted them true.

Now mix me a colour that nobody knows,
And paint me a country where nobody goes,
And put in it people a little like you,
Watching a unicorn drinking the dew.'

The Borrowers

Mary Norton

Pod, Homily and Arrietty are a family of tiny people who live under the floor of an old house. Everything that they have is borrowed from the 'human beans' who don't even know they exist. One day Homily sent her husband to get a cup from the children's toy set in the schoolroom of the house. When Pod returned, he had some bad news to tell.

Chapter four

Pod came in slowly, his sack on his back; he leaned his hat-pin, with its dangling name-tape, against the wall and, on the middle of the kitchen table, he placed a doll's tea-cup; it seemed the size of a mixing-bowl.

'Why, Pod –' began Homily.

'Got the saucer too,' he said. He swung down the sack and untied the neck. 'Here you are,' he said, drawing out the saucer. 'Matches it.'

He had a round, currant-bunny sort of face; tonight it looked flabby.

'Oh, Pod,' said Homily, 'you do look queer. Are you all right?'

Pod sat down. 'I'm fair enough,' he said.

'You went up the curtain,' said Homily. 'Oh, Pod, you shouldn't have. It's shaken you –' Pod made a strange face, his eyes swivelled round towards Arrietty.  Homily stared at him, her mouth open, and then she turned. 'Come along, Arrietty,' she said briskly, 'you pop off to bed, now, like a good girl, and I'll bring you some supper.'

'Oh,' said Arrietty, 'can't I see the rest of the borrowings?'

'Your father's got nothing now. Only food. Off you pop to bed. You've seen the cup and saucer.'

Arrietty went into the sitting-room to put away her diary, and took some time fixing her candle on the upturned drawing-pin which served as a holder.

'Whatever are you doing?' grumbled Homily. 'Give it here. There, that's the way. Now off to bed and fold your clothes, mind.'

'Good night, Papa,' said Arrietty, kissing his flat white cheek.

'Careful of the light,' he said mechanically, and watched her with his round eyes until she had closed the door.

'Now, Pod,' said Homily, when they were alone, 'tell me. What's the matter?'

Pod looked at her blankly. 'I been "seen",' he said.

Homily put out a groping hand for the edge of the table; she grasped it and lowered herself slowly on to the stool. 'Oh, Pod,' she said.

There was silence between them. Pod stared at Homily and Homily stared at the table. After a while she raised her white face. 'Badly?' she asked.

Pod moved restlessly. 'I don't know about badly. I been "seen". Ain't that bad enough?'

'No one,' said Homily slowly, 'hasn't never been "seen" since Uncle Hendreary and he was the first they say for forty-five years.'

✩ Why did Pod make 'a strange face' at Homily?

✩ What do you think is the significance of Pod 'been seen'?

106

A thought struck her and she gripped the table. 'It's no good, Pod, I won't emigrate!'

'No one's asked you to,' said Pod.

'To go and live like Hendreary and Lupy in a badger's set! The other side of the world, that's where they say it is – all among the earthworms.'

'It's two fields away, above the spinney,' said Pod.

'Nuts, that's what they eat. And berries. I wouldn't wonder if they don't eat mice –'

'You've eaten mice yourself,' Pod reminded her.

'All draughts and fresh air and the children growing up wild. Think of Arrietty!' said Homily. 'Think of the way she's been brought up. An only child. She'd catch her death. It's different for Hendreary.'

'Why?' asked Pod. 'He's got five.'

'That's why,' explained Homily. 'When you've got five, they're brought up rough. But never mind that now. . . Who saw you?'

'A boy,' said Pod.

'A what?' exclaimed Homily, staring.

'A boy.' Pod sketched out a rough shape in the air with his hands. 'You know a boy.'

'But there isn't – I mean, what sort of a boy?'

'I don't know what you mean "what sort of a boy". A boy in a night-shirt. A boy. You know what a boy is, don't you?'

'Yes,' said Homily, 'I know what a boy is. But there hasn't been a boy, not in this house, these 20 years.'

'Well,' said Pod, 'there's one here now.'

Homily stared at him in silence, and Pod met her eyes. 'Where did he see you?' asked Homily at last.

'In the schoolroom.'

'Oh,' said Homily, 'when you was getting the cup?'

'Yes,' said Pod.

'Haven't you got eyes?' asked Homily. 'Couldn't you have looked first?'

'There's never nobody in the schoolroom. And what's more,' he went on, 'there wasn't today.'

'Then where was he?'

'In bed. In the night-nursery or whatever it's called. That's where he was. Sitting up in bed. With the doors open.'

'Well, you could have looked in the nursery.'

'How could I – half-way up the curtain!'

'Is that where you was?'

'Yes.'

Why does Homily's tone change?

'With the cup?'
'Yes. I couldn't get up or down.'

'Oh, Pod,' wailed Homily, 'I should never have let you go. Not at your age!'
'Now, look here,' said Pod, 'don't mistake me. I got up all right. Got up like a bird, as you might say, bobbles or no bobbles. But' – he leaned towards her – 'afterwards – with the cup in me hand, if you see what I mean . . .' He picked it up off the table. 'You see, it's heavy like. You can hold it by the handle, like this. . . but it drops or droops, as you might say. You should take a cup like this in your two hands. A bit of cheese off a shelf, or an apple – well, I drop that . . . give it a push and it falls and I climbs down in me own time and picks it up. But with a cup – you see what I mean? And coming down, you got to watch your feet. And, as I say, some of the bobbles was missing. You didn't know what you could hold on to, not safely. . .'
'Oh, Pod,' said Homily, her eyes full of tears, 'what did you do?'
'Well,' said Pod, sitting back again, 'he took the cup.'
'What do you mean?' exclaimed Homily, aghast.
Pod avoided her eyes. 'Well, he'd been sitting up in bed there watching me. I'd been on that curtain a good ten minutes, because the hall clock had just struck the quarter –'
'But how do you mean – "he took the cup"?'

108

'Well, he'd got out of bed and there he was standing, looking up. "I'll take the cup," he said.' ⭐

'Oh!' gasped Homily, her eyes staring, 'and you give it to him?'

'He took it,' said Pod, 'ever so gentle. And then, when I was down, he give it me.' Homily put her face in her hands. 'Now don't take on,' said Pod uneasily.

'He might have caught you,' shuddered Homily in a stifled voice.

'Yes,' said Pod, 'but he just give me the cup. "Here you are," he said.'

Homily raised her face. 'What are we going to do?' she asked.

Pod sighed. 'Well, there isn't nothing we can do. Except –'

'Oh, no,' exclaimed Homily, 'not that. Not emigrate. Not that, Pod, now I've got the house so nice and a clock and all.'

'We could take the clock,' said Pod.

'And Arrietty? What about her? She's not like those cousins. She can *read*, Pod, and sew a treat –'

'He don't know where we live,' said Pod.

'But they look,' exclaimed Homily. 'Remember Hendreary! They got the cat and –'

'Now, now,' said Pod, 'don't bring up the past.'

'But you've got to think of it! They got the cat and –'

'Yes, but Eggletina was different.'

'How different? She was Arrietty's age.'

'Well, they hadn't told her, you see. That's where they went wrong. They tried to make her believe that there wasn't nothing but was under the floor. They never told her about Mrs Driver or Crampfurl. Least of all about cats.'

'There wasn't any cat,' Homily pointed out, 'not till Hendreary was "seen".'

> ⭐ What do you think was going through the boy's mind?

'Well, there was, then,' said Pod. 'You got to tell them, that's what I say, or they try to find out for themselves.'

'Pod,' said Homily solemnly, 'we haven't told Arrietty.'

'Oh, she knows,' said Pod; he moved uncomfortably. 'She's got her grating.'

'She doesn't know about Eggletina. She doesn't know about being "seen".'

'Well,' said Pod, 'we'll tell her. We always said we would. There's no hurry.'

Homily stood up. 'Pod,' she said, 'We're going to tell her tonight.'

What do you think happened to Eggletina?

1. How does the author describe Pod's face?
2. What was Pod and Homily's greatest fear?
3. Who saw Pod? Where was he when he was seen?
4. What did Homily mean by 'emigrate'?

5. Find examples in this extract which highlight the sense of scale.
6. What reasons did Homily give for not moving?
7. Pod and Homily spoke in an unusual way. Find examples of this.

8. Arrietty is a minor character in this extract but she plays an important role. What do you think this role is?
9. Who is the stronger character, Pod or Homily? Back up your answer with evidence from the text.
10. Do you think Pod and his family will have to move? Why?

11. What other things do you think Pod might 'borrow' from the 'human beans'?
12. Have you ever done something that took a lot of courage? Tell the class about it.
13. Choose your favourite section of dialogue in the extract. Re-read with a partner and act it out.

The Little Boy and the Old Man

Shel Silverstein

Said the little boy, 'Sometimes I drop my spoon.'
Said the little old man, 'I do that too.'
The little boy whispered, 'I wet my pants.'
'I do that too,' laughed the little old man.
Said the little boy, 'I often cry.'
The old man nodded, 'So do I.'
'But worst of all,' said the boy, 'it seems
Grown-ups don't pay attention to me.'
And he felt the warmth of a wrinkled old hand.
'I know what you mean,' said the little old man.

In the Nick of Time

Robert Swindells

Chapter one

A December morning, furred with frost. On iron ground, two people walk hand in hand, trailing plumes of breath through black bare trees. They are an old man and a girl of seven. Layers of clothing make their bodies shapeless, their movements stiff. The child speaks.

'There's nothing, Grandad. The birds have flown away, the squirrels and the flowers are asleep. What is there to look at in the woods?'

The old man gives the little hand a squeeze.

'We're in the midst of wonders, Charlotte, even on a day like today.' He smiles. 'It's a matter of knowing where to look.'

They come to an ice-bound pond, fringed with brittle stems of dead grasses. They stop. The little girl stares at the grey ice, the black leaves trapped inside it. Nothing can move. The old man looks down at his granddaughter. 'Seems lifeless, Charlotte, doesn't it?' The child nods, shivers. Stiffly her grandfather squats, hooks the fingers of both hands round the edge of a large flat stone, looks up with eyes that twinkle. 'Are you ready, Charlotte? Watch.'

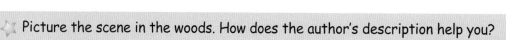

Gently, he lifts the stone. In the soft mud underneath, where frost can't penetrate, four crested newts lie sleeping. The child gazes, enthralled, breathes, 'What are they *doing*, Grandad: are they all right?'

The old man chuckles. 'They're hibernating, Charlotte, and they'll be absolutely fine till spring, when they'll wake up and fill the pond with brand new tadpoles.' Carefully he lowers the stone, straightens up with difficulty.

'Wonders, Charlotte. All around, all the time.' He smiles, takes her hand. 'Come on: Grandma'll have the breakfast on by now.' ⭐

Chapter two

I'm Charlie and I'm twelve. There's me, my nine-year-old brother Acton and our spaniel, Keeper. Oh, and Mum and Dad. I don't like school, and my hobbies are talking to friends on my moby and listening to music.

Monday morning of half term I'm in my room with a CD on when I hear Mum at the foot of the stairs.

'Charlotte?'

'What?' I sigh, knowing it'll be *turn that music down*, as usual, but it isn't.

'Grandma phoned. They've taken Grandad into hospital again. Dad and I are going over to sit with her for a while. D'you want to come?'

'No.'

'I'm sure she'd love to see you.'

'No, Mum, I can't.'

> ⭐ **What do you think he is trying to teach Charlotte?**

'Can't? What does *that* mean?'

'Means I can't, that's all'. I'll get *selfish* again, not to mention *moody* and *sulky*, but it isn't that. It's because I'm scared. My Grandad's dying and they think I don't know. Think I'm too young to handle the truth. They keep banging on about *when Grandad's better*. *When Grandad's better we'll all go away on holiday together*. Yeah, and pigs'll fly, right? We're close, Grandad and me. Always have been. He's not like other grown-ups. He doesn't talk down to me because I'm a kid, he assumes I'm an intelligent human being. Even when I was two he'd be like, *what'd you say to a gentle stroll down the path with an old man, Charlotte?* He gave me my full name before I grew into it, would've stuck needles in his eyes before using baby-talk, and he always listens properly when I'm telling him something. I guess what I'm trying to say is, Grandad and I respect each other. ✩

And it isn't as if I need to be told. You've only to look at Grandma's eyes, the way the light's gone out of them. And that's why I don't want to go. I can't stand to look at Grandma's eyes, but I won't say that to Mum.

She takes my brother instead, which means I can meet Pip without having to drag him along. Pip's my best friend. If anybody can help me forget about Grandad for a while, it's her.

I call her. I don't know it, but it won't be long before I'll be wishing I'd gone to Grandma's. ✩

✩ Think about Charlotte's relationship with her Grandad. Why are they so close do you think?

✩ What does Charlotte mean by this, do you think?

Chapter Three

We slog uphill to Cold Tarn* Woods. Not many people come here unless the tarn is frozen over and they can skate. It's February but there's no ice: global warming, I suppose. Pip hacks at the leafmould with the toe of her trainer. 'So what's he actually *got*, your grandad?'

'Some sort of cancer. I think it's in – you know, a part you don't mention.'

'Uh-huh. And it's doing your head in?'

'Yeah, well: I've always got on great with him, see? He's not like other old people: he's interested, keeps up with what's happening. You can have a conversation with him.'

'I know what you mean. My grandma and grandad don't know what I'm on about half the time. They're like, *iPod: what the heck's iPod*? It's as if they've already resigned from the world.' She stops, snatches at the sleeve of my jacket. 'Hey, look.'

We've come to where the trees thin out, giving way to a flattish area where gorse and bracken grow. I don't think I've ever seen it in winter before. The bracken's died back, and there's a big oblong of old concrete that must be hidden most of the year. We go over to it and I probe a crumbling edge with my toe. 'What d'you think it is?'

Pip shrugs. 'It's just a slab of cement now, but I suppose it was a floor at one time.'

'Floor of *what*, right up here?'

'Dunno. Army camp maybe. Scout camp. Holiday camp. Look: there's another over there, and another.'

We walk about, hacking at dead vegetation and peering into gorse bushes, and it turns out there's lots of floors, if that's what they are. Six at least. Most are the same size, but we find a couple that're bigger, square instead of oblong. I try to remember if I've ever heard anyone mention a camp up here, but I don't think I have.

'Look.' Pip's found another but I've seen something else: a pathway like a line of stepping stones, almost buried. I start to walk along it but there are gaps, like some stones are missing. I need big strides, even jumps. Landing after a long jump my foot skids on green slime and I fall, slashing my cheek on gorse. I wince, screw up my eyes against the sting. When I open them and blink away the tears, I'm lying on mown grass, surrounded by long, low buildings. There's no gorse, no pathway, no sign of Pip. Gripped by sudden dread, I scramble to my feet, glancing wildly around, seeing nothing I recognize. I start to sob; I can't help it, I must've gone mad or something. Hearing somebody behind me I whirl, hoping it's Pip, seeing instead a middle-aged woman who smiles and says, 'You must be Joyce Ingham, we've been expecting you.'

What do you think this means?

What do you think has happened to Charlotte?

* a small mountain lake or pond

Chapter four

'Mrs Livingstone –'

'Pip, is that you? Whatever's the matter, you sound –'

'It's Charlie, Mrs Livingstone, she's disappeared. I'm up by Cold Tarn Woods. She's just vanished.'

'Vanished? What d'you mean, vanished? People don't –'

'But she *has*, Mrs Livingstone, I've looked everywhere. There's these old floors, cement floors, and I called to Charlie and when she didn't answer I turned round and she'd gone. I've even tried phoning.'

'D'you think. . . might she be playing a trick on you: hiding somewhere?'

'There's nowhere to hide, Mrs Livingstone. I mean, there's the woods but she couldn't have reached them, not in the time.'

'There aren't holes, are there? Cellars, drains? She hasn't knocked herself out or. . .?'

'No, there's nothing like that, I've looked. I don't know what else to do.'

'Neither do I, Pip, to be perfectly honest. I mean, I don't want to get the police out, then find it's some sort of joke.'

'It's not a joke, Mrs Livingstone, I promise you that. I'm really, really scared.'

'All right, Pip, listen. Stay there, keep searching. I'm going to call the police, leave Acton with a neighbor and drive up. I'll be there as soon as I can, OK?'

'OK, Mrs Livingstone. . . bye.'

> How would you react if you were Charlotte's mother?

1. What wonders did Grandad show Charlotte?
2. What are Charlotte's hobbies?
3. What did Charlotte and Pip discover in Cold Tarn Woods?

4. Who is telling the story in each chapter? What effect does this have?
5. Scan the text and find words related to nature. Find out what they mean if they are new to you.
6. What kind of character is Charlotte? Find evidence in the extract to support your opinion.

7. How is Grandad different from other grandparents?
8. Why did Charlotte not want to visit her Grandma?
9. Why do you think the author began the story as he did?
10. Do you think Charlotte was right to refuse to visit her Grandma? Why? What would you have done?
11. What kind of relationship does Charlotte have with her mother?
12. What do you think will happen next?

13. In this story Charlotte has a great relationship with her Grandad. What other stories have you read where the main character is very close to a parent or grandparent?

From the Carnegie Medal-Winning author

ROBERT SWINDELLS

In the Nick of Time

Trees

1. List the names of all the trees you know.
2. What trees can you identify by a.) leaf, b.) fruit, c.) flowers, d.) twig?
3. Look at the headings. What do you already know about each one?

Types of tree

In general, trees can be divided into two groups, broad-leaved trees and coniferous trees.

Broad-leaved trees

Most broad-leaved trees are wide in shape and have flat, broad leaves. Broad-leaved trees need plenty of water and grow mainly in regions with mild temperatures. The horse-chestnut, the oak, the sycamore and the beech are the most common broad-leaved trees in Ireland. Most broad-leaved trees are also deciduous, that is they lose their leaves in autumn. But although the holly is a broad-leaved tree, it is also an evergreen.

Coniferous trees

A coniferous tree has long pointed leaves called needles and its seeds are carried in cones. The word 'conifer' means 'cone-carrying'. Conifers grow mainly in regions where weather conditions are harsh and summers are short. Conifers are tall and slender, and are mainly evergreen; they keep their leaves through the winter. The Scots pine, the yew and the juniper are the most common coniferous trees in Ireland. The larch, which also grows in Ireland, is a conifer, but it is not an evergreen.

The oak tree

Long ago, most of Ireland was covered with forests, mainly of oak. Then people arrived and began to cut down the trees. They needed timber to build houses and to make weapons and tools. The forests were also cleared to make space for growing crops and cattle-grazing.

As Ireland's population grew more forests were chopped down. The timber was used for shipbuilding, barrel-making and for building large houses, castles and cathedrals. Irish oak was exported and was used for building abroad. It was even used in building the Houses of Parliament in England. Today, only small areas of Ireland are covered with native oak woods.

The oak is a deciduous tree that grows up to 30 metres in height. A fully-grown oak tree has about 150,000 leaves. Ireland's national tree is the sessile oak.

- In a good year, the crop of acorns from a mature oak will weigh about 1, 350 kilogrammes – the same weight as 16 fully grown men. There will be up to 50,000 acorns in this crop. Only one in a million acorns survives to become a tree. The rest are eaten by animals, such as insects and squirrels.

- A large oak can support up to 400,000 caterpillars at one time.

- Many different types of birds, including the wagtail and the chaffinch, feed on the caterpillars who feed on the leaves of the tree.

- Goodness released from the decay of the fallen leaves returns back to the soil, only to be taken up again by the roots of other trees. Roots take up water and minerals from the soil, they hold the tree in place and they help to keep the soil from being washed away. If a root is blocked by a stone, it grows around the stone.

- Many oak trees have galls. These are caused when insects lay their eggs in the tree. The wart-like growths surround the growing insect. The gall prevents the insect from attacking the tree while the insect is sheltered inside the gall. Birds peck at galls to get at the insect inside.

Did you know?

The Irish for oak is 'dair' and it appears in a number of Irish placenames, such as Cill Dara (Kildare), Áth Dara (Adare) and Doire (Derry). Think of others.

The name Daragh, also spelt Dara or Daire, means 'little oak' in Irish!

Trees are by far the largest, oldest and tallest living thing on this planet.

Evergreen trees do in fact lose some of their leaves, but not all at the same time as in the case of deciduous trees.

To work out a tree's age, measure the girth and divide it by 2.5.

The coastal redwoods or sequoias of the USA are thought to be the tallest trees in the world. The tallest tree standing today is the 'Mendocino Tree'. It measures 112 metres and is estimated to be 1,000 years old.

The smallest tree in the world is the dwarf willow. Some are only five centimetres tall.

The eucalyptus is the fastest growing tree in the world. A tree in New Guinea grew by 10.5 metres in one year!

A Norwegian spruce on Campbell Island, Antarctica, is believed to be the most remote tree. Its nearest companion is more than 222 kilometres away.

About 30 per cent of air pollution produced in Europe by factories, houses and cars is absorbed by Europe's forests. Trees help to reduce pollution by taking in carbon dioxide from the air.

Trees and insects

Here is a list of trees found in Ireland and the number of insect species they support. Which trees would you plant to support the greatest number of insects?

Native trees	Insects	Non-native trees	Insects
Oak	284	Beech	64
Willow	266	Spruce	37
Birch	229	Lime	31
Hawthorn	147	Larch	17
Scots pine	91	Sycamore	15
Ash	41	Sweet chestnut	5
Holly	7	Horse chestnut	4

The food factory

The tree, just like all green plants, makes its own food. The tree's food is made in its leaves. Because leaves contain a green substance called chlorophyll, they can trap energy from the sunlight. Leaves are carefully arranged on each tree to catch the maximum amount of sunlight possible. They use this energy, along with carbon dioxide from the air and water from the soil, to make food which is sent to other parts of the tree to help it grow. This process is called photosynthesis.

1. What are the differences between broad-leaved and coniferous trees?
2. What is photosynthesis?
3. What gas do trees a.) absorb and b.) give off?
4. Make a list of other a.) broad-leaved and b.) coniferous trees.
5. What new terms have you learned in this unit? Explain what each one means.
6. Research some other interesting facts about trees around the world.
7. Choose a tree and find out as much as you can about it. Bring a leaf, twig, flower or fruit into the class.

Grow an oak tree

1. Test your acorns. Carefully remove the 'cup' from each acorn and put the acorns in a basin of water. Some acorns will sink to the bottom while others will float on the water's surface. The heavier, healthier acorns sink to the bottom. These are the ones to plant.

2. Place the small stones at the bottom of each flowerpot for drainage. Fill each pot with the mixture of soil and potting compost. Make one hole in each pot of soil about 5cm deep.

3. Put one acorn into each hole and cover it with soil.

4. Place the pots outside in winter, where they will not be disturbed. Make sure the soil is kept moist and that the pots get enough sunshine in spring.

5. In spring, the shoot of the young tree will appear. Keep the tree in the pot for two years. Make sure that you water it regularly.

6. After two years, plant the tree outside. This must be done between the months of November and March.

Stopping by Woods on a Snowy Evening

Robert Frost

Whose woods these are I think I know.
His house is in the village, though;
He will not see me stopping here
To watch his woods fill up with snow.

My little horse must think it queer
To stop without a farmhouse near
Between the woods and frozen lake
The darkest evening of the year.

He gives his harness bells a shake
To ask if there is some mistake.
The only other sound's the sweep
Of easy wind and downy flake.

The woods are lovely, dark, and deep,
But I have promises to keep,
And miles to go before I sleep,
And miles to go before I sleep.

War Horse

Michael Morpurgo

Joey is a young half-thoroughbred colt who has just been sold at auction. His new owner is a hard, bitter man who treats him roughly but his son Albert forms a strong bond with the horse.

Chapter two

Through the long hard winters and hazy summers that followed, Albert and I grew up together. A yearling colt and a young lad have more in common than awkward gawkishness.

Whenever he was not at school in the village, or out at work with his father on the farm, he would lead me out over the fields and down to the flat, thistly marsh by the Torridge river. Here on the only level ground on the farm he began my training, just walking and trotting me up and down, and later on lunging me first one way and then the other. On the way back to the farm he would allow me to follow on at my own speed, and I learnt to come at his whistle, not out of obedience but because I always wanted to be with him. His whistle imitated the stuttering call of an owl – it was a call I never refused and I would never forget. ⭐

Old Zoey, my only other companion, was often away all day ploughing and harrowing, cutting and turning out on the farm and so I was left on my own much of the time. Out in the fields in the summer time this was bearable because I could always hear her working and call out to her from time to time, but shut in the loneliness of the stable in the winter, all day could pass without seeing or hearing a soul, unless Albert came for me.

As Albert had promised, it was he who cared for me, and protected me all he could from his father; and his father did not turn out to be the monster I had expected. Most of the time he ignored me and if he did look me over, it was always from a distance. From time to time, he could even be quite friendly, but I was never quite able to trust him, not after our first encounter. ⭐

⭐ Who is telling this story?

⭐ What might have happened in the first encounter?

I would never let him come too close, and would always back off and shy away to the other end of the field and put old Zoey between us. On every Tuesday however, Albert's father could still be relied upon to get drunk, and on his return Albert would often find some pretext to be with me to ensure that he never came near me.

On one such autumn evening about two years after I came to the farm Albert was up in the village church ringing the bells. As a precaution he had put me in the stable with old Zoey as he always did on Tuesday evenings. 'You'll be safer together. Father won't come in and bother you, not if you're together,' he'd say, and then he'd lean over the stable door and lecture us about the intricacies of bell-ringing and how he had been given the big tenor bell because they thought he was man enough already to handle it and that in no time he'd be the biggest lad in the village. My Albert was proud of his bell-ringing prowess and as Zoey and I stood head to tail in the darkening stable, lulled by the six bells ringing out over the dusky fields from the church, we knew he had every right to be proud. It is the noblest of music for everyone can share it – they have only to listen. ⭐

I must have been standing asleep for I do not recall hearing him approach, but quite suddenly there was the dancing light of a lantern at the stable door and the bolts were pulled back. I thought at first it might be Albert, but the bells were still ringing, and then I heard the voice that was unmistakably that of Albert's father on a Tuesday night after the market. He hung the lantern above the door and came towards me. There was a whippy stick in his hand and he was staggering around the stable towards me.

'So, my proud little devil,' he said, the threat in his voice quite undisguised. 'I've a bet on that I can't have you pulling a plough inside a week. Farmer Easton and the others at The George think I can't handle you. But I'll show 'em. You've been

⭐ What are your first impressions of Albert?

125

molly-coddled enough, and the time has come for you to earn your keep. I'm going to try some collars on you this evening, find one that fits, and then tomorrow we'll start ploughing. Now we can do it the nice way or the nasty way. Give me trouble and I'll whip you till you bleed.'

Old Zoey knew his mood well enough and whinnied her warning, backing off into the dark recesses of the stable, but she need not have warned me for I sensed his intention. One look at the raised stick sent my heart thumping wildly with fear. Terrified, I knew I could not run, for there was nowhere to go, so I put my back to him and lashed out behind me. I felt my hooves strike home. I heard a cry of pain and turned to see him crawling out of the stable door dragging one leg stiffly behind him and muttering words of cruel vengeance.

That next morning both Albert and his father came out together to the stables. His father was walking with a pronounced limp. They were carrying a collar each and I could see that Albert had been crying for his pale cheeks were stained with tears. They stood together at the stable door. I noticed with infinite pride and pleasure that my Abert was already taller than his father whose face was drawn and lined with pain. 'If your mother hadn't begged me last night, Albert, I'd have shot that horse on the spot. He could've killed me. Now I'm warning you, if that animal is not ploughing straight as an arrow inside a week, he'll be sold on, and that's a promise. It's up to you. You say you can deal with him, and I'll give you just one chance. He won't let me go near him. He's wild and vicious, and unless you make it your business to tame him and train him inside that week, he's going. Do you understand? That horse has to earn his keep like everyone else around here – I don't care how showy he is – that horse has got to learn how to work. And I'll promise you another thing, Albert, if I have to lose that bet, then he has to go.' He dropped the collar on the ground and turned on his heel to go.

'Father,' said Albert with resolution in his voice. 'I'll train Joey – I'll train him to plough all right – but you must promise never to raise a stick to him again. He can't be handled that way, I know him, Father. I know him as if he were my own brother.'

'You train him, Albert, you handle him. Don't care how you do it. I don't want to know,' his father said dismissively. 'I'll not go near the brute again. I'd shoot him first.'

But when Albert came into the stable it was not to smoothe me as he usually did, nor to talk to me gently. Instead he walked up to me and looked me hard in the eye. 'That was divilish stupid,' he said sternly. 'If you want to survive, Joey, you'll have to learn. You're never to kick out at anyone ever again. He means it, Joey. He'd have shot you just like that if it hadn't been for Mother. It was Mother who saved you. He wouldn't listen to me

What might the consequences be?

Do you think Albert will succeed? Why?

and he never will. So never again Joey. Never.' His voice changed now, and he spoke more like himself. ⭐ 'We have one week Joey, only one week to get you ploughing. I know with all that thoroughbred in you you may think it beneath you, but that's what you're going to have to do. Old Zoey and me, we're going to train you; and it'll be divilish hard work – even harder for you 'cos you're not quite the right shape for it. There's not enough of you yet. You won't much like me by the end of it, Joey. But Father means what he says. He's a man of his word. Once he's made up his mind, then that's that. He'd sell you on, even shoot you rather than lose that bet, that's for sure.'

That same morning, with the mists still clinging to the fields and linked side by side to dear old Zoey in a collar that hung loose around my shoulders, I was led out on to the Long Close and my training as a farmhorse began. As we took the strain together for the first time the collar rubbed at my skin and my feet sank deep into the soft ground with the effort of it. Behind, Albert was shouting almost continuously, flashing a whip at me whenever I hesitated or went off line, whenever he felt I was not giving it my best – and he knew. This was a different Albert. Gone were the gentle words and the kindness of the past. His voice had a harshness and a sharpness to it that would brook no refusal on my part. Beside me old Zoey leant into her collar and pulled silently, head down, digging in with her feet. For her sake and for my own sake, for Albert's too, I leant my weight into my collar and began to pull. I was to learn during that week the rudiments of ploughing like a farm horse. Every muscle I had ached with the strain of it; but after a night's good rest stretched out in the stable I was fresh again and ready for work the next morning.

Each day as I progressed and we began to plough more as a team, Albert used the whip less and less and spoke more gently to me again until finally at the end of the week I was sure I had all but regained his affection. Then one afternoon after we had finished the headland around Long Close, he unhitched the plough and put an arm around each of us. 'It's all right now, you've done it my beauties. You've done it,' he said. 'I didn't tell you, 'cos I didn't want to put you off, but Father and Farmer Easton have been

⭐ Why did Albert change his tone of voice?

watching us from the house this afternoon.' He scratched us behind the ears and smoothed our noses. 'Father's won his bet and he told me at breakfast that if we finished the field today he'd forget all about the incident, and that you could stay on, Joey. So you've done it my beauty and I'm so proud of you I could kiss you, you old silly, but I won't do that, not with them watching. He'll let you stay now, I'm sure he will. He's a man of his word is my father, you can be sure of that – long as he's sober.'

It was some months later, on the way back from cutting the hay in Great Meadow along the sunken leafy lane that led up into the farmyard that Albert first talked to us of the war. His whistling stopped in mid-tune. 'Mother says there's likely to be a war,' he said sadly. 'I don't know what it's about, something about some old Duke that's been shot at somewhere. Can't think why that should matter to anyone, but she says we'll be in it all the same. But it won't affect us, not down here. We'll go on just the same. At fifteen I'm too young to go anyway – well that's what she said. But I tell you Joey, if there is a war I'd want to go. I think I'd make a good soldier, don't you? Look fine in a uniform, wouldn't I? And I've always wanted to march to the beat of a band. Can you imagine that, Joey? Come to that, you'd make a good war horse yourself, wouldn't you, if you ride as well as you pull, and I know you will. We'd make quite a pair. God help the Germans if they ever have to fight the two of us.' ⭑

One hot summer evening, after a long and dusty day in the fields, I was deep into my mash and oats, with Albert still rubbing me down with straw and talking on about abundance of good straw they'd have for the winter months, and about how good the wheat straw would be for the thatching they would be doing, when I heard his father's heavy steps coming across the yard towards us. He was calling out as he came. 'Mother,' he shouted. 'Mother, come out Mother.' It was his sane voice, his sober voice and was a voice that held no fear for me. 'It's war, Mother. I've just heard it in the village. Postman came in this afternoon with the news. The devils have marched into Belgium. It's certain for sure now. We declared war yesterday at eleven o'clock. We're at war with the Germans. We'll give

⭑ Do you think Albert knows what war is really like? Why?

them such a hiding as they won't ever raise their fists again to anyone. Be over in a few months. It's always been the same. Just because the British lion's sleeping they think he's dead. We'll teach them a thing or two, Mother – we'll teach them a lesson they'll never forget.'

Albert had stopped brushing me and dropped the straw on the ground. We moved over towards the stable door. His mother was standing on the steps by the door of the farmhouse. She had her hand to her mouth. ' Oh dear God,' she said softly. 'Oh dear God.'

> What thoughts are going through his mother's head, do you think?

1. What did Joey do whenever Albert's Dad tried to get close to him?
2. Which church bell was Albert responsible for ringing?
3. Why did Albert think it would be difficult for Joey to learn to plough?

4. There are many words related to horses and farming in this story. Scan through the text and make a list. Talk about them.
5. Albert's father could be intimidating at times. Find examples in the text that show this.
6. Joey loved Albert. Where can you see this in the extract?
7. How did Albert train Joey to plough?
8. How did Albert's parents react to the news of the war?

9. Why did Albert's Dad take on the bet, do you think?
10. Do you think Albert would make a good soldier? Why?
11. What kind of relationship does Albert have with a.) his father and b.) his mother?
12. Authors often include minor characters in the text. Name a minor character in this chapter and say why you think the author included him/her.
13. What might happen later in the book?

14. Find out all you can about World War I.
15. Explore which was the longest and the shortest war in history.

Horses

1. Talk about any books you have read or films you have seen that feature horses.
2. Examine the picture of the horse. Which numbered parts can you name?
3. Make a list of as many words as you can that are linked with horses e.g. stallion, gallop etc.

Horses have been used by humans for more than 5,000 years. We have used them in farming, in transport, in sport and in war.

Know your horse

Colours

Horses come in different colours, including black, brown, chestnut (reddish-brown), dun (yellowish-grey), grey and white. Adult horses with white coats are usually called 'greys'. Piebald horses have large, irregular patches of black and white, while skewbald horses have large patches of white and any colour other than black.

Piebald

Skewbald

1. Ears
Horses have a keen sense of hearing. A horse's ear can turn to detect where a sound is coming from. Certain positions of the ears can tell about a horse's mood; for example, an angry horse lays his ears back flat.

2. Withers
Horses are measured in hands. One hand is equal to 10cm, the average width of a man's hand. Measurement is made from the ground to the highest point of the withers.

3. Coat
A horse's body is covered in a coat of hair. A thick winter coat grows every autumn and is shed every spring.

4. Tail
A horse uses its tail to brush away flies.

5. Hind legs
These provide power for running and jumping. Horses can reach speeds of 65 kilometres an hour.

6. Forelegs
These carry most of the horse's weight. Horses can sleep while standing up. They lock special joints in their legs to keep themselves upright.

7. Hooves
Each foot has a strong hard hoof made of bone. Most horses wear horseshoes which are made of metal and fitted by farriers.

8. Teeth
Horses have strong teeth. Most male horses have 40 teeth while most females have 36. Horses eat only grain and plants, never meat. Experts can tell the age of a horse by the number and size of its teeth, together with the way they have been worn down with use.

9. Mane
The hair of a horse's mane or the tail is never shed. If the hair becomes too thick, it may be pulled. This does not hurt a horse as there are no nerves at the roots of its hair.

The Horse in World War I (1914–1918)

The Cavalry

During World War I, horses played a significant role. The cavalry were soldiers who fought while mounted on horseback. The cavalry charge was used as part of a shock tactic in attacks on enemy trenches. Many armies stopped using horses in battle soon after the war began, as they proved easy targets for machine gun and artillery fire. Tanks, which were invented during the war, replaced the cavalry charge. As the war progressed, horses were mainly used for transporting supplies to the Front, for carrying messengers and for pulling artillery, ambulances and supply wagons. Horses were sure-footed over rough terrain. Today, most cavalry units serve in ceremonial roles only.

Unlike many other armies, the British army continued to use mounted infantry and cavalry charges during the war. At the start of World War I, the British army had 25,000 horses but within two weeks a further 154,000 were secured. Horses aged between three and 12 years were trained by British soldiers called 'roughriders'. This was done as quickly as possible before the horses were transported by ship to the battlefields. The strongest horses were used by the cavalry as those horses had to carry a soldier plus the additional weight of the soldier's equipment, saddle and ammunition. The soldiers were encouraged to dismount as often as possible to ease the burden on the horse. Other horses were used to help with transportation. In 1914, the British army had only 80 motor vehicles, so horses were essential for transporting goods and supplies. Muddy conditions underfoot also made it difficult to use the early type of motor vehicles they had at that time.

At the Front

Conditions at the Front were severe for the horse. Getting fodder for them was very difficult and many horses died from starvation. A horse was allowed about nine kilogrammes of grain a day which was only three-quarters of the amount it was fed in peacetime. The 'war horse' was always hungry.

Taken out of their environment, whether field or city, factory or coal-pit, the horses were shipped off to war, a world away from home. Over 8,000,000 horses from both sides died between 1914 and 1918.

Horse sense

However quiet a horse seems, any strange sounds or actions could startle it. Here are a few hints on how to approach a horse:

Always speak to a horse before approaching it. Speak quietly to it and do not make any sudden movements.

A horse can see almost all around itself but has a blind spot behind it, so you should always warn a horse before you walk behind it. Run your hand over its back and hindquarters, so that it knows where you are.

When feeding a horse a titbit, always keep your hand flat and your fingers together.

Some parts of a horse are ticklish. Be careful when touching ticklish places like its stomach or flanks!

1. Go back to the list of 'horse' words you made at the beginning. You should now be able to add to it.

2. How should you behave when approaching a horse?

3. Why did many countries stop using the cavalry charge during World War I?

4. How did horses help with transportation during World War I?

5. How are horses used today (think about work, sport, pleasure, industry)?

6. Ireland is famous for its horse industry. Find out more by checking out the Irish National Stud website: www.irish-national-stud.ie

7. Choose one of the following and find out as much as you can about it: Pegasus, Black Beauty, Shergar, the unicorn.

8. Research World War I. The following headings might help: reasons for the war; countries involved; outcome of the war; military tactics used during the war (tanks, poison gas, trench warfare). Find out as much as you can and present your findings to the class. This website will help you get started: www.historylearningsite.co.uk

Skulduggery Pleasant

Derek Landy

When twelve-year-old Stephanie's rich Uncle Gordon dies and leaves his house to her in his will, she ends up spending the night in the house on her own. As Stephanie is getting ready for bed, a strange man smashes in through one of the windows and attacks Stephanie. She is in real danger, when suddenly Skulduggery Pleasant bursts through the door flinging it off its hinges; he grapples with the intruder and fights him off. When Stephanie realises that Skulduggery is a skeleton with magic powers, it all becomes too much for her and she faints.

Stephanie awoke on the couch with a blanket over her. The room was dark, lit only by two lamps in opposite corners. She looked over at the broken window, saw that it was now boarded up. She heard a hammering from the hall, and when she felt strong enough to stand, she slowly rose and walked out of the living room.

Skulduggery Pleasant was trying to hang the door back on its hinges. He had his shirtsleeve rolled up on his left forearm. *Ulna*, Stephanie corrected herself, proving that her first year of Biology class had not gone to waste. Or was it *radius*? Or both? She heard him mutter, then he noticed her and nodded brightly.

'Ah, you're up.'

'You fixed the window.'

'Well, covered it up. Gordon had a few pieces of timber out back, so I did what I could. Not having the same luck with the door though. I find it much easier to blast them off than put them back. How are you feeling?'

'I'm OK,' Stephanie said.

'A cup of hot tea, that's what you need. Lots of sugar.'

He abandoned the door and guided her to the kitchen. She sat at the table while he boiled the water.

'Hungry?' he asked when it had boiled, but she shook her head. 'Milk?' She nodded. He added milk and spoonfuls of sugar, gave the tea a quick stir and put the cup on the table in front of her. She took a sip – it was hot, but nice.

'Thank you,' Stephanie said, and he gave a little shrug. It was hard discerning some of his gestures without a face to go by, but she took the shrug to mean 'think nothing of it'.

'Was that magic? With the fire, and blasting the door?'

'Yes, it was.'

She peered closer. 'How can you talk?'

'Sorry?'

'How can you talk? You move your mouth when you speak, but you've got no tongue, you've got no lips, you've got no vocal cords. I mean, I know what skeletons look like, I've seen diagrams and models and stuff, and the only things that hold them together are flesh and skin and ligaments, so why don't you just fall apart?'

He gave another shrug, both shoulders this time. 'Well, that's magic too.'

She looked at him. 'Magic's pretty handy.'

'Yes, magic is.'

'And what about, you know, nerve endings? Can you feel pain?'

'I can, but that's not a bad thing. Pain lets you know when you're alive, after all.'

'And are you alive?'

'Well, *technically*, no, but. . .'

She peered into his empty eye sockets. 'Do you have a brain?'

He laughed. 'I don't have a brain, I don't have any organs, but I have a consciousness.' He started clearing away the sugar and the milk. 'To be honest with you, it's not even my head.'

'What?'

'It's not. They ran way with my skull. I won this one in a poker game.'

'That's not even yours? How does it feel?'

'It'll do. It'll do until I finally get around to getting my own head back. You look faintly disgusted.'

'I just. . . Doesn't it feel weird? It'd be like wearing someone else's socks.'

'You get used to it.'

'What happened to you?' she asked. 'Were you born like this?'

'No, I was born perfectly normal. Skin, organs, the whole shebang. Even had a face that wasn't too bad to look at, if I do say so myself.'

'So what happened?'

Skulduggery leaned against the worktop, arms folded across his chest. 'I got into magic. Back then – back when I was, for want of a better term, alive – there were some pretty nasty people around. The world was seeing a darkness it might never have recovered from. It was war, you see. A secret war, but war nonetheless. There was a sorcerer, Mevolent, worse than any of the others, and he had himself an army, and those of us who refused to fall in behind him found ourselves standing up against him.

'And we were winning. Eventually, after years of fighting this little war of ours, we were

> What do you think of Skulduggery so far?

> How do you think Stephanie feels talking to a skeleton?

actually winning. His support was crumbling, his influence was fading, and he was staring defeat in the face. So he ordered one last, desperate strike against all the leaders on our side.'

Stephanie stared at him, lost in his voice.

'I went up against his right-hand man who had laid out a wickedly exquisite trap. I didn't suspect a thing until it was too late. ⭐

'So I died. He killed me. The twenty-third of October it was, when my heart stopped beating. Once I was dead, they stuck my body up on a pike and burned it for all to see. They used me as a warning – they used the bodies of all the leaders they had killed as warnings – and, to my utter horror, it worked.'

'What do you mean?'

'The tide turned. Our side starting losing ground. Mevolent got stronger. It was more than I could stand, so I *came back*.'

'You just. . . came back?'

'It's. . . complicated. When I died, I never moved on. Something was holding me here, making me watch. I've never heard of it happening before that and I haven't heard of it happening since, but it happened to me. So when it got too much, I woke up, a bag of bones. Literally. They had gathered up my bones and put them in a bag and thrown the bag into a river. So that was a marvellous new experience right there.'

'Then what happened?'

'I put myself back together, which was rather painful, then climbed out of the river and rejoined the fight, and in the end, we won. We finally won. So, with Mevolent defeated, I quit that whole scene and struck out on my own for the first time in a few hundred years.'

Stephanie blinked. 'Few hundred?'

'It was a long war.' ⭐

'That man, he called you detective.'

'He obviously knows me by reputation,' Skulduggery said, standing a little straighter. 'I solve mysteries now.'

'Really?'

'Quite good at it too.'

'So, what, you're tracking down your head?'

Skulduggery looked at her. If he'd had eyelids, he might well be blinking. 'It'd be nice to have it back, sure, but. . .'

'So you don't need it, like, so you can rest in peace?'

'No. No, not really.'

> ⭐ In what way might Skulduggery have been trapped?

> ⭐ This is a fantasy story. What do you think is most unbelievable so far?

'Why did *they* take it? Was that another warning?'

'Oh, no,' Skulduggery said with a little laugh. 'No, *they* didn't take it. I was sleeping, about ten or fifteen years ago, and these little goblin things ran up and nicked it right off my spinal column. Didn't notice it was gone till the next morning.'

Stephanie frowned. 'And you didn't feel that?'

'Well, like I said, I was asleep. Meditating, I suppose you'd call it. I can't see, hear or feel anything when I'm meditating. Have you tried it?'

'No.'

'It's very relaxing. I think you'd like it.'

'I'm sorry, I'm still stuck on you losing your head.'

'I didn't lose it,' he said defensively. 'It was stolen.'

Stephanie was feeling stronger now. She couldn't believe that she'd fainted. *Fainted*. It was such an old woman thing to do. She glanced up at Skulduggery. 'You've had a very unusual life, haven't you?'

'I suppose I have. Not over yet though. Well, *technically* it is, but. . .'

'Isn't there anything you miss?'

'About what?'

'About living.'

'Compared to how long I've been like this, I was only technically alive for a blink of an eye. I can't really remember enough about having a beating heart in my chest to miss it.'

'So there's nothing you miss?'

'I. . . I suppose I miss hair. I miss how it. . . was. And how it was there, on top of my head. I suppose I miss my hair.' ⭐

He took out his pocket watch and his head jerked back. 'Wow, look at the time. I've got to go, Stephanie.'

'Go? Go where?'

'Things to do, I'm afraid. Number one is finding out why that nice gentleman was sent here, and number two is finding out who sent him.'

'You can't leave me alone,' she said, following him into the living room.

'Yes,' he corrected, 'I can. You'll be perfectly safe.'

'The front door's off!'

'Well, yes. You'll be perfectly safe as long as they don't come through the front door.'

He pulled on his coat but she snatched his hat away.

'Are you taking my hat hostage?' he asked doubtfully.

'You're either staying here to make sure no one else attacks me or you're taking me with you.'

Skulduggery froze. 'That,' he said eventually, 'wouldn't be too safe for you.'

'Neither would being left here on my own.'

⭐ What would you miss most if you were a skeleton?

137

'But you can hide,' he said, gesturing around the room. 'There's so many places to hide. I'm sure there are plenty of good solid wardrobes your size. Even under a bed. You'd be surprised how many people don't check under beds these days.'

'Mr Pleasant –'

'Skulduggery, please.'

'Skulduggery, you saved my life tonight. Are you going to undo all that effort by leaving me here so someone else can come along and just kill me?'

'That's a very defeatist attitude you've got there. I once knew a fellow, a little older than you. He wanted to join me in my adventures, wanted to solve mysteries that beggared belief. He kept asking, kept on at me about it. He finally proved himself, after a long time, and we became partners.'

'And did you go on to have lots of exciting adventures?'

'I did. He didn't. He died on our very first case together. Horrible death. Messy too. Lots of flailing around.'

'Well, I don't plan on dying any time soon and I've got something he didn't.'

'And that is. . . ?'

'Your hat. Take me with you or I'll stand on it.'

Skulduggery looked at her with his big hollow eye sockets, then held out his hand for his hat. 'Don't say I didn't warn you.'

1. What did Skulduggery make for Stephanie when she woke up?
2. What is unusual about Skulduggery's head?
3. Why did Skulduggery's enemies stick his body up on a pike?

4. Skulduggery is considerate towards Stephanie. Find examples of this.
5. Stephanie asked Skulduggery lots of questions. Which questions do you think were the most interesting or unusual?
6. Although this has been a frightening, weird experience for Stephanie, there is a lot of humour in the extract. Which part do you think is the funniest?
7. Who do you think is the most important character in the extract? Why do you think this?

8. What kind of character is Stephanie?
9. How do you think you would have reacted to Skulduggery? What questions would you have asked him?
10. Why do you think Skulduggery 'never moved on' after dying?
11. Describe what might happen next in the story.

12. Skulduggery has magic powers. Who is your favourite character with magic powers from a book or a film? Describe the character and the special powers he or she has.
13. This is a story of good and evil. What is your favourite book or film in which good fights against evil?

DEREK LANDY

Skulduggery
Pleasant
THE DEAD FAMOUS BESTSELLER

From cover to cover

1. A book is made up of many parts. Name as many of these as you can.
2. How many different kinds of books can you name?
3. What is the best a.) fiction b.) non-fiction book you have read?

In this unit, we will examine the different sections of a book. We will look at a table of contents, a glossary and an index. Knowing how to use these is a valuable skill that can save you time when you want to access information quickly. Even the cover can give you clues as to what a book is about.

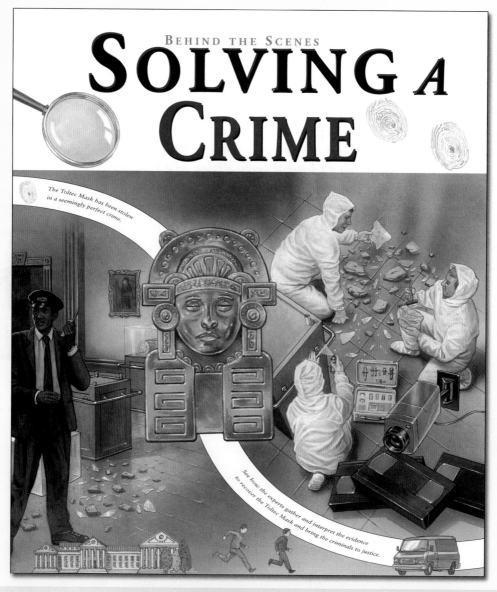

4. Examine the front cover of this book. Describe the stolen object and the scene of the crime.

CONTENTS

5. Examine the table of contents. In which chapters might you find out about:
   a.) Taking a statement from a witness?
   b.) Prosecuting a case?
   c.) Fingerprint dusting?
   d.) Ways of protecting valuables?
   e.) Somebody who was wrongly accused of a crime?

INDEX

1. Look down through the index. Make a list of words that relate to:
   a.) security b.) museums c.) forensics d.) courtroom.
2. How can an index help you?
3. Which index entry has the highest number of page references?
4. Scan the index to find the name of the stolen object.
5. Make a list of all the topics you could read about on a.) pages 5 and b.) 20.

GLOSSARY

Alibi
Proof that you were somewhere else when a crime happened.

Closed circuit television
Television cameras linked by wires to TV screens and video recorders usually in the same building.

Curator
The person in charge of a museum.

DNA
A complicated chemical found coiled up inside the nucleus of every living cell.

DNA profile
A pattern of bands made from a person's DNA. Each person has his/her own distinct pattern.

Evidence
Clues and other facts which help to show that a person did or did not carry out a particular crime.

Fingerprint
An almost invisible pattern made from sweat and grease on fingertips which is left behind on a smooth surface. Each person leaves his/her own particular pattern.

Fingerprint dusting
Coating surfaces with fine powder and then blowing gently. The powder sticks only to the fingerprints and shows up the pattern.

Forensic Scientist
A scientist who uses scientific equipment to collect clues and to examine them as evidence for use in a court of law.

Forensic Team
The detectives who look for clues which can be used as evidence against criminals.

Incident room
The place at a police station where detectives collect clues together and meet to discuss ideas about solving a crime.

Infra-red rays
A type of light which is invisible to human eyes but which electric sensors can detect.

Interpol
Short for the International Police Commission, which shares information between the police forces of different countries.

Plaster cast
A copy of footprints or dents, made by pouring liquid plaster into the imprint and allowing the plaster to set.

Prosecution lawyer
An expert in the law who tries to show that the evidence is clearly linked to the suspects.

Surveillance equipment
All the sensors, closed circuit TV cameras, monitor screens, and alarms which help security officers to survey, or watch, the whole of a building all the time.

1. Find a word in the glossary for the following definitions:
   a.) A person in charge of a museum.
   b.) A person who uses scientific equipment to collect evidence.
   c.) Facts that help show that a person committed a crime.
   d.) A chemical found inside the nucleus of every living cell.
2. How is a glossary different from a dictionary? How can a glossary help you when you are reading?
3. Choose another word from the index and create a glossary definition for it. Where would you put it in the glossary?
4. In groups, choose a topic that you have read about in this book and devise a glossary for it.

Call of the Whales

Siobhán Parkinson

Tyke goes with his anthropologist father to the remote icy wilderness of the Arctic. He has adventures there, such as joining a whale hunt, and makes new friends including an Inuit called Henry. In this extract Henry has been swept away on an ice floe.

Chapter fourteen: Tyke to the Rescue

I wandered off along what we thought of as the shore, but was really the point where the frozen sea met the watery sea. I was further up the coast, a bit away from the spot where the whale had been landed and the big clean-up operation was going on. I could hear the murmur of work and the occasional shout on the air, but I was pretty much out of actual earshot. All I could see of the villagers, when I looked over my shoulder, was constant movement up and down the icy shoreline as men and boys and girls and women moved about, packing and readying themselves for the homeward journey.

In one direction, the ice stretched in a glaring white expanse for miles and miles. It was enough to give you a headache looking at it, there was so much gleaming, retina-stretching white. In the other direction was the indigo expanse of the ocean. Since it was spring and the ice was breaking up, small sections of the icy shore were constantly breaking off and drifting out to sea, so that the surface of the water was dotted with the glittering debris of the break-up, little flat ice islands and odd half-melted lumps of ice like tiny icebergs jostling their way along, bumping off each other, drifting together some times, and then floating off again.

Overhead the sky was the bluest blue you can imagine, an icy, terrifying blue, far bluer than the skies you see in hot places, and streaked with feathery white cloud on the horizon. There was so much ice and so much sea, so much white and so much blue, that I thought we'd never find Henry. You could walk for miles on the icy shore, calling his name, and all you'd see would be blue and white and white and blue, broken only by the huge inky shapes of the bow-heads flickering through the sea like giant shadows, making large dark zeppelins under the surface, with an occasional dark shape drifting elephantinely to the surface, its blow erupting through the deep blue water into silvery fountains.

I walked the endless ice away from the noise and the bustle of the camp and the stench of food and blood and oil and into the icy blue wilderness. I concentrated on Henry, imagining that if I thought hard enough about him, I could conjure up an image of where he was in my head.

Every now and then, I scanned the horizon, pointlessly as I thought, but then something seemed to flutter on one of the drifting ice floes way out to sea. I screwed my eyes and sure enough, the flutter came again. Someone was moving about, waving, on one of the drifting ice floes. It had to be Henry. I waved back, throwing all my strength into the movement of my arms, to assure him that I'd seen him.

I turned then and yelled for my dad. I yelled and yelled till my throat hurt, but it was several minutes since he'd left. He'd evidently walked out of earshot by now. I started to run in the direction he'd gone, but then I stopped. It could take me ages to catch him. By then Henry might have floated off out of sight, and I'd never find him in the huge, heaving expanse of sea and float-ice.

What do you think Tyke is feeling here?

If I'd had time to think I'd never have done it, but I was in such a panic my body acted on its own. There were umiaqs everywhere about. I leapt into one, loosely tethered to a grappling iron driven into the ice. I undid the rope that held it, and pushed it away from the ice shore. It was only after I'd got it out on the water that I thought to look for oars. The boat was full of things – a small stove, a harpoon, a gun and, thank heavens, paddles. I'd never rowed even a little rowing boat, much less manned a boat of this size, heavy with equipment, across an expanse of arctic sea, bobbing with ice islands, but somehow I managed to get it moving roughly in the direction I wanted it to go. I kept my eyes fixed on Henry's drifting ice floe. He was yelling to me. I could hear his cries floating on the icy air, but I couldn't hear what he was trying to tell me. I knew I had to reach him. I had to. If I didn't rescue him, he could go floating off and over the horizon and never be heard of again. It happens to arctic hunters all the time, one of the hazards of their way of life. ☆

'I'm coming!' I yelled, but I knew he couldn't possibly hear me. Still, it helped to shout it. It kept me going.

I paddled and paddled, but I didn't seem to be getting any closer. Was I going around in circles? I thought I must be, because I was only paddling on one side. I grabbed another paddle and tried to use them like oars, but the boat was too wide for me. I couldn't reach across it to use two paddles at once.

I stood up and paddled frantically from one side, then, unsteadily, I slithered to the other side of the boat and paddled a bit more on that side. Slowly, slowly, the boat moved in wide arcs. It wasn't exactly going in circles, but it was zigzagging forward only very slowly. Most of the movement was sideways, in the sweep of the arcs. I could see this was a problem, but it was the only way I could make the umiaq move at all, so I kept paddling, wriggling from one side to the other and paddling, paddling, paddling furiously.

Every now and then, I looked up to check if I could still see Henry. Every time I looked, he seemed further away, but I could hear his panic-stricken cries and I kept heading for him, though I was getting exhausted.

At last – it seemed like hours – I started to get closer. Each time I looked up, he seemed a little larger, a little easier to make out. I came close enough to hear his voice, as distinct from just yells, to hear actual words. He was shouting directions. He stood on the edge of his ice floe, which was bobbing along with slow, almost dreamy movements on the swell of the sea, and yelled instructions at me. He understood boats better than I did, so I listened.

'Paddle from the left,' he was shouting. 'Keep going. OK now, quickly, from the right. Quick, quick, she's circling, stop her! Good, good, now a few more goes on the right. Now run to the other side. . .'

☆ Do you think Tyke is doing the right thing?

Slowly, slowly, the boat swung closer and closer to Henry's ice floe, but every time we were about to make contact, the ice floe drifted tantalizingly away again. It was like trying to catch an ice cube in a sink with wet fingers. I can't, I thought. I can't do it. I'm too tired. It won't do what I want.

'Just keep coming,' yelled Henry. 'You are getting closer. You are. Just don't lose your nerve, don't panic and don't tire.'

My arms were taut as iron rods by now with the effort of paddling, and the constant evasive action of the ice floe was beginning to wear me down, but Henry's shouts kept me concentrated on what I was doing.

Eventually, I felt the umiaq make contact with the ice with a gentle bump. The mild impact propelled the boat back again, but with the next paddle we made contact again, like a currach nosing in to a harbour wall. On the third impact, Henry's outstretched arm brushed mine, and on the fourth attempt, he took a flying, floundering leap and landed in the umiaq like a huge, thrashing fish. The boat rocked dangerously with the impact, and hit off the ice floe several times, but I steadied it by bracing my feet against the sides, and gradually it settled on the water.

Henry scrambled off the floor and, keeping his body bent to prevent overturning the boat, he managed to sit down.

'Hey, Henry!'

He looked smaller than himself, and his body was shaking, shaking, his face white and thin.

Is Henry younger or older than Tyke? Why do you think this?

'Hey, Tyke!' he said, his voice wobbly and small. He looked as if he was trying to smile, but he couldn't manage it.

He leaned over the side of the boat then and projected a stream of vomit out over the sea.

I stared at him, listening helplessly to his retching. It was only when I saw him getting sick that I realised how close he'd been to death, how scared he must have been. I started to feel scared myself, then – up to then I'd felt only panic and unnamed terror, but now it was real, logical, believable fear, fear of death, fear of drowning, fear of never seeing my dad again. Mum, I thought suddenly. Oh, Mum! I felt bile rise in own throat. I swallowed hard and looked away, determined not to join Henry in getting sick. Somebody had to keep upright, and it would have to be me.

Henry turned to me then, still half-hanging over the side of the boat, vomit-streaked snot hanging from his nose, and I could feel the shaking of his body rocking the boat.

'Here,' I said, and I threw a hanky at him. 'Wipe up.'

He wiped his streaming face with the handkerchief and then he held it out to me.

'Yuck!' I said, and pulled away from it.

'Oh, sorry,' he said with half a smile.

He trailed the hanky in the water, wrung it out and wiped his face with it again. He bunched the wet hanky up then and threw it in the bottom of the boat.

'That's better,' Henry said, and picked up a paddle.

'You OK?' I asked.

'I'll live,' he said and leant over the side of the boat to help me manoeuvre it away from the ice floe. We paddled furiously, but without co-ordination, and so instead of moving the boat away from the island, we rammed it back against the edge of the ice with double-force, and, with a sickening scrunch, the prow of the boat wedged itself into a crevice in the ice and we were stuck fast.

Henry pushed against the ice with his paddle, but the boat wouldn't budge. I leant over and we both pushed and heaved with all our might, but we didn't have much strength left between us, and the umiaq had embedded itself in the ice. It wouldn't give an inch.

'What'll we do?' I wailed. My teeth were chattering now, with fear as much as cold, and my body was shaking from the efforts I was making to shift the boat.

'One of us is going to have to get off the umiaq and back onto the ice floe,' said Henry, 'and use the paddle to lever the boat away from the ice.'

'Not me,' I said quickly. I knew my own limits. I'd probably slip, I'd probably fall into the water, I'd probably die. I knew what a spill into the arctic waters could do. I could feel the pain of the freezing water gripping my limbs without so much as a splash getting on my skin.

How do you think Henry and Tyke get on?

148

'Me then,' said Henry.

I stared at him, and he stared back. I couldn't see how he was going to muster either the strength or the courage to get back off the boat, having just made it aboard. I'd have cowered in the boat and refused to move.

'But it's moving!' My voice was thin and high with anxiety. I couldn't believe this was happening to us, that my dad and Henry's dad were less than a quarter of a mile away and here we were going to be lost at sea.

'Yup,' said Henry, his eyes scrunched up in concentration. 'Still, that's the only way we can get the umiaq loose. Otherwise we're going to drift off all the way to the North Pole.' ⭐

Something about the idea of the North Pole froze my heart. I imagined a maypole, spiralling red and white like a barber's pole, and me and Henry slumped at the bottom of it, waiting for a polar bear to come along and gobble us both up.

Henry stood up unsteadily and then, with a sudden spurt of energy, he leapt off the boat and back onto the ice floe. He stood on the ice floe again and kicked the edge of the umiaq with all his force. Nothing happened. He kicked again and again, and then he prised his paddle into the crevice and at last, with a groan, the boat released itself and bobbed out, away from the ice. Henry took another flying leap and landed in the boat as it floated away. There was another awful moment as the boat rocked and rocked and rocked, steadying itself from the impact of Henry's leap, but it settled as it had before. Henry lay slumped against the side of the boat for a while, gathering his strength.

'You OK?' I asked again.

He nodded wearily, then sat up straight and picked up a paddle.

With two of us paddling, the umiaq moved more swiftly and in a perceptible direction. I felt my heart begin to lift as the shore came closer. We were going to survive. It was only when I thought that, that I fully realized how close we had come to not surviving. I looked at Henry, and he was looking at me.

'Hey, Henry,' I said again.

'Hey, Tyke,' he said and grinned. ⭐

But we weren't home yet. We still had an expanse of water to cross, with only a flimsy boat between us and the freezing ocean. We paddled away for a bit, saying nothing, concentrating on keeping the boat moving.

I looked over the edge into the water and thought about how many miles down it was to the depthless bottom and how many tons of water were under the boat, and

⭐ What do you learn about Henry here?

⭐ Why do you think the two boys don't express their feelings more?

149

as I looked, a shadow nudged by, a huge, huge shadow, like a submarine only much swifter and more graceful.

'Henry,' I said, in as low a voice as I thought he could hear. 'There's a whale on this side of the boat. It's close enough to touch.'

I remember thinking as I said that, that this was the realisation of my dreams, to be within touching distance of a bowhead whale. I never thought I ever would be, and I certainly never thought that if I was, I would be alone on the ocean with another boy in a skin boat and in danger of being capsized at any moment by a casual flick of the whale's tail.

'Hmm,' said Henry, his voice also low, hardly more than a whisper, 'there's one on this side too. But whatever you do, don't touch it, Tyke. Pull your paddle in.'

I didn't need to be told a second time. I drew my paddle in as calmly and quietly as I could, and we both sat huddled together, our paddles dripping ice-cold sea-water onto the flat floor the boat. We sat silently, drifting casually, like two people out for a little leisurely boating and taking a break from the hard work of making the craft move, but knowing that we were in danger of being flicked over at any moment. Even if we didn't drown, we would probably die of hypothermia if we hit the water and down our bodies would go, cold and twirling, to the bottom of the sea. I shuddered at the thought.

We practically held our breaths, allowing the air to escape from our bodies only very slowly and quietly, desperate to make ourselves invisible, inaudible, not there.

> How do you think the boys felt when they realised the whales were under their boat?

> How do you think you might react in this situation?

Occasionally a whale breached, its huge body suddenly ungainly out of the water, lumbering as a hippopotamus. One whale let out its giant blow so close that we were both drenched in the warm, salty, fishy mist of its breath, and we could hear its soft whining calls, as if it was talking, complaining, to itself. But still we sat motionless in our boat, and waited for all the whales to swim by.

They kept coming, pod after pod of them, with short gaps in between, swishing and flickering, always avoiding the boat, though they swam very near to it. It was as if they were aware it was there, and they were swimming around the obstruction it caused on the surface. We could see the swift movements of their tails as they swam, displacing the water and propelling them forward, and occasionally we saw a whale nose an ice floe out of the way.

Still they came, and still we sat, and the sky started to get that flushed look I now knew was the beginning of the sunset. My shoulders ached, partly with the effort of paddling, but mostly with the effort of sitting still. My feet were like two overgrown ice cubes slithering about in the bilge-water on the floor of the boat. And still we sat and still the whales swam by.

At last, they passed on, but even after we ceased to see the great underwater shadows and to hear their whines and soft screeches, we sat still for a long time, just in case, in the air that seemed to reverberate with the whales' yearning hoots even after they'd swum out of earshot.

Henry shifted beside me and expelled a long, sighing out breath. He stretched then and picked up his paddle. I did the same, and soon we were moving to the shore again, our aching limbs urging the boat forward as the sky deepened.

'Wasn't that. . .' I cast about for a word. 'Scary' came to mind, but although it had been scary, that wasn't the word I wanted. '. . . weird?' I finished, though 'weird' wasn't really the word I wanted either.

'Weird,' said Henry. 'Almost. . . what's that word? Mystical.'

A little shiver went through me when he said it. That was the word I'd wanted, but I'd probably have been embarrassed to say it even if I could have thought of it.

I nodded, but then the spell was broken and I laughed. It was all too much, and we needed to break the terrible tension.

'Verrry myshticle,' I said, exaggerating my Irish accent. 'Verry, verry myshticle indeed. That was a very myshticle shower of whale blow, wasn't it. Myshticle and mishty, ahh!' Henry laughed too and his shoulders shook.

We laughed, but then we were only boys. We didn't know how to talk about it, but we knew it was true. It *had* been mystical.

> Why was it important to break the tension?

We paddled on for a bit, and then I said: 'I wouldn't blame them if they'd killed us.
'Who?' asked Henry.
'The whales.'
'Why would they want to kill us?'
'Because we killed one of them.'
'Yes, but that was a hunt,' said Henry. 'We didn't kill the whale out of anger.'
'What difference does that make? You kill it, it's dead.'
'All the difference. If we were fighting the whales, if we were killing them for fun or because we wanted to get rid of them, then they would be angry. But when we hunt, we pray for the whale, we ask the whale to give itself to feed the people. We release its spirit. There's no need for anger. That's just how things are. The whales know that.'
He sounded very sure of himself, but I couldn't agree. How could the whales know a thing like that? It didn't make any sense. And I noticed that for all his talk, Henry had been just as anxious as I was not to disturb the whales when they swam near our boat. But I didn't argue. I just kept paddling.
'Like the bear in the story,' Henry added.
'What?'
'The bear in the story. The story is about how the people and the animals help each other.'
Yes, but that's a fairytale, I thought to myself, but I didn't say so out loud.
We made much better progress with the umiaq now that there were two of us and pretty soon the ice shore seemed reachable. There were figures standing about on the ice, watching us. They seemed to be getting umiaqs ready to come out to meet us, but I think when they saw that we were making good progress, they held back. As we came closer, I saw that two of the people were my dad and Henry's dad and they had a pair of binoculars that they kept passing from one to the other. When they could see us getting closer, they started punching each other encouragingly on the upper arms and hallooing and roaring and waving their arms at us.
'How on earth did you manage an umiaq on your own?' asked Dad, as he put out his hand to help me ashore.
'I have absolutely no idea,' I said, putting my foot on 'dry land'. The words came out like washing from a wringer, all stretched and squeezed. It seemed to hurt my chest to talk. That's the last thing I remember, my dad's hand under my elbow and my feet touching the pack ice. My dad said I collapsed at his feet. Exhaustion, he said. I don't think so. I think it was sheer relief.

> Whose point of view do you agree with?

1. What was in the boat that Tyke took?
2. What happened when a whale surfaced?

3. This extract is full of danger. How do the boys react?
4. Henry has more experience of the Arctic than Tyke. Find evidence of this in the chapter.
5. There are some interesting similes in this chapter. Find examples.
6. Make a list of the words or phrases in the first three pages which describe the landscape.

7. How do you think Henry became cut off from the others?
8. Which part of Tyke's experience do you think he found the most frightening or dangerous?

9. Have you ever visited a country with a cold, snowy climate? Tell the class about what makes it different or special.
10. This story is set in the Arctic. What do you know about this part of the world?
11. Besides whales, what other animals do humans hunt? Do you think it is right to hunt animals? Give two reasons for and two reasons against the hunting of animals.
12. Have you ever helped to rescue someone or some animal? Have you ever had to be rescued? Talk about it.

Call of the Whales

Siobhán Parkinson

Sea Fever

John Masefield

I must go down to the seas again, to the lonely sea and the sky,
And all I ask is a tall ship and a star to steer her by,
And the wheel's kick and the wind's song and the white sail's shaking,
And a grey mist on the sea's face, and a grey dawn breaking.

I must go down to the seas again, for the call of the running tide
Is a wild call and a clear call that may not be denied;
And all I ask is a windy day with the white clouds flying,
And the flung spray and the blown spume, and the sea-gulls crying.

I must go down to the seas again, to the vagrant gypsy life,
To the gull's way and the whale's way where the wind's like a whetted knife;
And all I ask is a merry yarn from a laughing fellow-rover,
And quiet sleep and a sweet dream when the long trick's over.

Artemis Fowl

Eoin Colfer

How does one describe Artemis Fowl?
Various psychiatrists have tried and
failed. The main problem is Artemis's
own intelligence. He bamboozles every
test thrown at him. He has puzzled the
greatest medical minds and sent many of them
gibbering to their own hospitals.

There is no doubt that Artemis is a
child prodigy. But why does someone of such
brilliance dedicate himself to criminal
activities? This is a question that can
be answered by only one person. And he
delights in not talking.

Perhaps the best way to create an
accurate picture of Artemis is to tell
the by now famous account of his first
villainous venture. I have put together
this report from first-hand interviews
with the victims, and as the tale unfolds
you will realize that this was not easy.

This story began several years ago at
the dawn of the 21st century.
Artemis Fowl had devised a plan to
restore his family's fortune. A plan that
could topple civilizations and plunge the
planet into a cross-species war.

He was twelve years old at the time . . .

Of course, it had started with the Internet. But then it always does.

Alien abductions. UFO sightings. Ley lines. Ancient stone circles.

And the People. It always came back to the People.

Trawling through gigs of data, he had compiled a database from the thousands of references to fairies he'd found from countries all over the world.

Each human civilization had its own term for the People. But there was no doubt that the reports referred to the same hidden race.

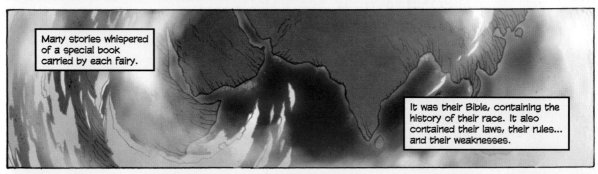

Many stories whispered of a special book carried by each fairy.

It was their Bible, containing the history of their race. It also contained their laws, their rules... and their weaknesses.

Any human who came into possession of such a book would have an entirely new species to exploit.

Of course, this book was said to be written in Gnommish, so even if someone could steal a copy, it would be of absolutely no use to any human.

CHAPTER 1:
THE BOOK

At least, any ordinary human...

I HOPE THIS ISN'T ANOTHER WILD-GOOSE CHASE, *BUTLER.*

ESPECIALLY AFTER OUR LITTLE MISHAP IN CAIRO.

NO, SIR. I'M CERTAIN THIS TIME. NGUYEN IS A GOOD MAN.

Ho Chi Minh City in the summer. Or Saigon, as the locals still called it. Sweltering by anyone's standards.

There seems no end to the crowds. Even the alleyways are full to bursting. Cooks smile and drop fish heads into woks of hissing oil. There's a new smell on every corner.

HMM, AFTER SIX FALSE ALARMS SPREAD OVER THREE CONTINENTS, I HOPE SO.

I BELIEVE THE CAFÉ IS LEFT AT THE NEXT JUNCTION, SIR.

A TABLE FOR SOME TEA, SIR? I'LL BE YOUR WAITER.

YOU ARE WEARING A SILK SHIRT AND THREE GOLD SIGNET RINGS. YOUR ENGLISH HAS A TINGE OF OXFORD ABOUT IT AND YOUR NAILS HAVE THE SOFT SHEEN OF HAVING BEEN RECENTLY MANICURED. YOU ARE NOT A WAITER. YOU, SIR, ARE OUR CONTACT.

SIT DOWN, *NGUYEN.*

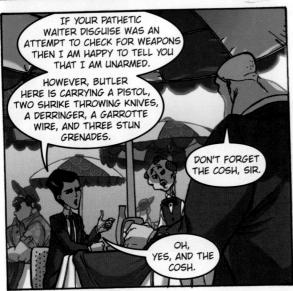

IF YOUR PATHETIC WAITER DISGUISE WAS AN ATTEMPT TO CHECK FOR WEAPONS THEN I AM HAPPY TO TELL YOU THAT I AM UNARMED.

HOWEVER, BUTLER HERE IS CARRYING A PISTOL, TWO SHRIKE THROWING KNIVES, A DERRINGER, A GARROTTE WIRE, AND THREE STUN GRENADES.

DON'T FORGET THE COSH, SIR.

OH, YES, AND THE COSH.

I KNOW WHERE YOU CAN FIND WHAT YOU ARE SEARCHING FOR.

EXPLAIN.

'This woman. She is a healer, near Tu Do Street. She heals in exchange for rice wine. All the time, drunk. She is what you seek, Mister... Master Fowl.'

AND NOW YOU'LL TAKE US TO HER.

NO, NO. INFORMATION ONLY. THAT WAS THE AGREEMENT. I DON'T WANT A CURSE ON MY HEAD.

I'M SORRY, MR NGUYEN, BUT THE TIME WHEN YOU HAD A CHOICE IN THESE MATTERS IS LONG PAST.

'If you have brought us to the end of our quest, Mr Nguyen, you will be well rewarded. If you have wasted our time, I am afraid Butler will not be pleased.'

IT SEEMS WE MUST PROCEED ON FOOT. RUN IF YOU LIKE, BUT EXPECT A SHARP AND FATAL PAIN BETWEEN YOUR SHOULDER BLADES IF YOU DO.

'Don't worry. I won't run.'

SHE'S UNDER THERE. SHE NEVER GOES OUT. NOT EVEN TO BUY RICE SPIRITS.

BUTLER, THE GOGGLES PLEASE.

159

MADAM, I HAVE A PROPOSITION FOR YOU.

GIVE ME DRINK.

The gift of tongues.

Check.

Aversion to light.

Check.

PLEASE PAY OUR FRIEND, BUTLER, IN FULL.

AND, REMEMBER, MR. NGUYEN, THIS STAYS JUST BETWEEN US.

MY LIPS ARE SEALED.

'They had better be. Or Butler here will seal them permanently.'

NOW, MADAM, TO BUSINESS. I MUST CONFESS, I DO NOT WANT HEALING. APART FROM A SLIGHT ALLERGY TO DUST MITES, I AM PERFECTLY HEALTHY.

NO, WHAT I WANT FROM YOU IS YOUR BOOK.

YOU WANT BOOK? GO LIBRARY.

YOU ARE NO HEALER. YOU ARE A SPRITE, A FAIRY, A KA-DALUN. AND I WANT YOUR BOOK.

IF YOU KNOW ABOUT THE BOOK, HUMAN, THEN YOU KNOW I HAVE ENOUGH MAGIC IN ME TO KILL YOU WITH A SNAP OF MY FINGERS!

161

MAKE SURE YOU PHOTOGRAPH EVERY PAGE. AND EMAIL THE IMAGES HOME AS SOON AS YOU'RE DONE.

OF COURSE, SIR.

'No use to you anyway.

'Written in the old tongue.'

YOUR NEEDLES HAVE STRONG MAGIC.

I'M AFRAID THE AMNESIAC MIXED INTO THE SECOND INJECTION MEANS THAT YOU WON'T REMEMBER US.

GOOD.

'Time to leave, Butler. A hundred years of alcohol leaving a body by any means possible is not going to be a pretty sight.'

'Thank you, madam.

"It's been a pleasure doing business with you.'

162

NAME:
Artemis Fowl the Second

CLASSIFICATION:
VERY DANGEROUS

KNOWN PSEUDONYMS AND ALIASES:
Dr F. Roy Dean Schlippe, Stefan Bashkir,
Emmsey Squire

SPECIALIZED SKILLS:
Possibly possesses the greatest human intellect
of his generation

Perhaps any generation, but you can't believe everything he says.

NAME:
Butler

FIRST NAME:
D CENSORED

CLASSIFICATION:
Bodyguard

BACKGROUND:
The Butlers have been serving the Fowls for centuries.
Several eminent linguists believe this is how the noun originated.

SPECIALIZED SKILLS:
SAS-level marksmanship, martial arts including Cos Ta'pa, emergency
medicine, information technology, and cordon bleu cooking. The subject
is fluent in several languages. Believed to have studied extensively
under the Japanese sensei Madame Ko. Spent several years working
freelance in the espionage arena, including stints for the British
and French secret service.

DISTINGUISHING FEATURES:
Blue diamond tattoo on shoulder

WEAPON OF CHOICE:
Sig Sauer

KNOWN ALIASES:
Constantin Bashkir, Colonel Xavier Lee

KNOWN RELATIONS:
Juliet—younger sister
'The Major'—his uncle, believed to have been killed when the CENSORED

The Seven Wonders of the World

1. What do you think is meant by a 'Wonder of the World'?
2. Scan the headings in this unit. Look carefully at the illustrations. Which of the Seven Wonders can still be seen today?

The Seven Wonders of the World make up one of the most famous lists ever compiled, but few people can name them all. What is meant by 'world' is that part of the world around the Mediterranean Sea, the centre of ancient Roman and Greek civilisation. There were many wonders in the ancient world and people often discussed which were the most awe-inspiring. About 130BC, a Greek writer compiled a list of these wonders. They are described here in order of age, beginning with the oldest.

1. The Pyramids at Giza

The only Wonder still standing today is the pyramids at Giza in Egypt which were built about 4,500 years ago. The pyramids were and still are the largest stone buildings in the world. They were built as royal tombs for the Pharaohs, the rulers of ancient Egypt. The largest of the pyramids, the Great Pyramid of Cheops, is nearly 140 metres high, and was built using 2.3 million blocks of stone. Each block weights about 2.5 tonnes! The pyramids were built close to the river Nile so that the massive blocks could be transported by river from the quarry to the pyramid site. The blocks were then moved on sledges or rollers over the ground. Each pyramid was constructed by thousands of slaves, an undertaking that could take 20 or 30 years to complete. Such great skill and precision were used in placing the stones that it was impossible to push even a hair into the joints between them!

Tutankhamun

Tutankhamun is perhaps the best known of Egypt's Pharaohs. He became Pharaoh at the age of nine and died just nine years later. His tomb is in the Valley of the Kings, near Luxor in southern Egypt. It was discovered by the English archaeologist, Howard Carter, and his patron, Lord Carnarvon, in 1922. When the two men entered the tomb, they were amazed at what they saw. As well as the mummified body of the Pharaoh enclosed in a stone sarcophagus, there was an amazing collection of objects. These gave great insights into how people lived more than 3,000 years ago: clothes, weapons, jewellery, wines, preserved foods, beds, chairs, even a chariot! A trumpet was found that could still be played. Most of the contents of the tomb were removed to the National Museum in Cairo.

2. The Hanging Gardens of Babylon

The Hanging Gardens were built by the King of Babylon in about 600BC for one of his queens. The gardens consisted of a number of terraced roof gardens that rose in a pyramid shape over 90 metres into the air. Plants and flowers from all over the known world were used. They concealed the framework of the structure so that the gardens seemed to hang unsupported in the air. It is not known when the gardens were destroyed and scientists have been unable to identify positively the remains of the gardens. It is thought the gardens were located close to where the city of Baghdad is today.

3. The Temple of Artemis at Ephesus

Artemis was the Greek goddess of the moon and hunting. The temple to the goddess was built in about 550BC at Ephesus, on the coast of Turkey. It was built at the expense of King Croesus, who is thought to have been the richest king in the world in ancient times. It was said that it was built on marshy ground to protect it against future earthquakes. It was more than 120 metres long and the roof was supported by over 100 columns. Each column was 18 metres high. The temple, made mainly from marble, was famous for its beautiful sculptures and other works of art. The original temple took 120 years to complete. It was burned down in 356BC and was rebuilt on the same foundation. The second temple was destroyed about 600 years later by invading tribes but its foundations and some debris have survived. The site of the temple was discovered in 1869 and excavations were carried out.

4. The Statue of Zeus at Olympia

In Greek mythology, Zeus was the king of the gods. At Olympia, in Greece, there was a famous temple to Zeus where people came to worship him. Inside was a huge statue in his honour. The statue was built in about the year 433BC. It was 12 metres high and was as wide as the temple's aisle. Gold, ivory and precious stones were used in its decoration. In the statue's right hand was a small statue of Nike, the goddess of victory, and in the left hand Zeus held a shining sceptre with an eagle perched on top. The statue was so impressive, people said, that if you looked at it, you would forget all your troubles. The statue was destroyed in 394AD.

5. The Mausoleum at Halicarnassus

When the wealthy King Mausolus died in about the year 353BC, his widow had a great tomb built for him at Halicarnassus in south-west Turkey. The tomb was of white marble and was decorated by skilled craftspeople. Mausolus was cremated and his ashes were laid in an underground tomb, beneath the memorial.

The tomb was destroyed in an earthquake in the 15th century and only fragments remain today. Apart from the pyramids, the mausoleum lasted longer than any of the other Wonders. The word 'mausoleum' which comes from Mausolus's name, is now used to describe any large tomb.

6. The Colossus of Rhodes

Rhodes is a Greek island off the coast of Turkey. The Colossus of Rhodes was a statue built by the people of Rhodes in about the year 290BC to guard the entrance to the island's harbour. The gigantic statue, which measured 32 metres in height, was made of bronze and stood on a marble base beside the harbour. It represented the Greek sun god Helios. The statue was about the same size as the Statue of Liberty and is thought to have been the inspiration for it. The statue collapsed during an earthquake 56 years after being built and for hundreds of years its remains lay scattered on the ground. It was eventually sold to an Arab merchant, carried off on the backs of 900 camels and broken up for scrap! Today we use the word 'colossal' to describe something that is enormous.

7. The Pharos of Alexandria

The Pharos of Alexandria was a very tall lighthouse built about 280BC on the island of Pharos, at the entrance to the port of Alexandria in Egypt. It was built by the Egyptian Pharaoh, Ptolemy II, and was the most famous lighthouse of ancient times. Pictures of the lighthouse even appeared on Roman coins! It rose to a height of about 125 metres and it is said that its light could be seen from a distance of 65 kilometres. Huge fires were lit at night and large curved mirrors focused the light into a powerful beam. In the day the sun's rays were used. The lighthouse stood for about 1,700 years, but was eventually destroyed in an earthquake. To this day it remains the tallest lighthouse ever built. In the 1990s, archaeologists began exploring underwater ruins off the coast near Alexandria. Among these were ruined statues that may have decorated the Pharos.

Did you know?

The curse of Tutankhamun: at the time of the discovery of the tomb, some people felt that those who had entered it were guilty of sacrilege and that bad luck would follow them. Five months after he entered the tomb, Lord Carnarvon was bitten by a mosquito and died later of pneumonia.

The head of the Colossus of Rhodes was believed to have been modelled on the Greek hero, Alexander the Great.

It is claimed that a mirror at the top of the Pharos of Alexandria reflected events in Byzantium (Istanbul) which was 1,250 kilometres away.

The Temple of Artemis was the largest of all ancient Greek buildings.

The city of Alexandria was named after the famous Greek king, Alexander the Great. In ancient times more than 15 cities were named after him, most of them no longer in existence.

1. List as many of the Seven Wonders as you can in order of:
   a.) height
   b.) dates when they were destroyed.
2. Choose one character mentioned in the unit and find out as much as you can about him or her.
3. Which of the Wonders would you most like to have visited? Why?
4. Choose one of the Wonders and find out more about it.

The Seven New Wonders of the World

1. Look at the illustrations. What do you know about any of the Wonders?
2. Can you name other buildings or structures that might be considered Wonders of the Modern World?
3. Make a list of Wonders in Ireland.

In 2007, the New 7 Wonders Foundation, a Swiss organisation, published the results of a worldwide poll that it held to find the Seven Wonders of the modern world. Although one of the original Seven Wonders, the Pyramids, is still intact, it was decided not to include them in the list of new wonders. It was claimed that more than 100 million people took part in the poll by internet or by phone.

The seven modern wonders to emerge from the poll were:
1. The Colosseum (Italy)
2. The Taj Mahal (India)
3. Petra (Jordan)
4. Machu Picchu (Peru)
5. The Statue of Christ the Redeemer (Brazil)
6. The Great Wall of China (China)
7. Chichen Itza (Mexico)

The Colosseum

This building, which could seat over 50,000 people, was completed in 80AD during the reign of the emperor Titus. It was used to amuse and entertain the people of Rome with its fierce fights between gladiators, and between slaves and wild animals; men were indeed thrown to the lions. It even hosted mock sea battles during which the arena was flooded. Its ruins today are one of Rome's most popular sights for tourists.

The Taj Mahal

When the emperor Shah Jahan's wife died giving birth to their 14th child more than 300 years ago, her heartbroken husband had this beautiful building built as a memorial tomb to her. It took 21 years and more than 22,000 workers to complete the project. Located in Agra in northern India, the Taj Mahal is a world heritage site today and is considered by many as the most beautiful building in the

world. It has a dome of white marble and more than 28 different kinds of precious gems and stones pressed into its walls. More than 1,000 elephants were used to bring materials to the site.

Petra

The city of *Petra* – the name means rock in Greek – was built about the year 600 BC, carved into the red rock of mountains in Jordan. Enormous skill was required to carve temples, passageways and other buildings out of the bare rock. It is sometimes called the City of Tombs because of the many tombs built into the rock face. At one time Petra was a busy thriving city, with

camel caravans laden with spices, jewels and gold carrying their goods from Damascus to Arabia. Then for hundreds of years it became a quiet, half-forgotten backwater – the lost city of stone – until it was discovered in the last century. Because of its dramatic setting it was chosen as the location for scenes in the film, *Indiana Jones and the Last Crusade*.

Machu Picchu

The ancient Inca city of Machu Picchu high up in the Andes mountains of Peru was discovered in 1911. Archaeologists were amazed at what they found... ruins of temples, a royal palace and even the remains of an aqueduct that brought water to the city. Most amazing of all, they found an *intihuatana*, a pyramid the Incas constructed to speak to their gods. The city was built about 500 years ago for the Inca emperor and was inhabited for just 100 years until the Spanish conquered the country. Today Machu Picchu, which is part of the Inca Trail, is Peru's top tourist attraction.

Statue of Christ the Redeemer

This statue was built in Rio de Janeiro, Brazil in 1931 as a symbol of peace. Perched on a mountain overlooking the city it is nearly 40 metres tall and took nine years to construct. The statue, which weighs over 600 tonnes, is made of concrete to support the statue's outstretched arms. It is one of the largest statues in the world. In 2008, the statue was struck by lightning which damaged the fingers and head.

The Great Wall of China

The Great Wall of China stretches for thousands of kilometres from China's east coast to the Gobi desert in the northwest. Construction of the wall began about the year 200BC when the Emperor Qin decided to connect the different existing walls and fortifications within his empire.

The project continued for over 1,700 years as emperor after emperor sought to improve China's defences against outside attack. Hundreds of thousands of people were involved in the building. They received no payment and many died during construction, as rocks fell and sections of wall caved in. Some died from sheer exhaustion. It is regarded as one of the most impressive building projects in human history. The Chinese say that the wall resembles a huge dragon winding its way over the mountains.

Chichen Itza

In Chichen Itza, marvellous archaeological remains of the Mayan civilisation can be found. They were a highly sophisticated race of people who lived in Mexico before the time of Columbus. The site contains a wide range of buildings, the most famous of which is the step pyramid, called El Castillo. It was built about 1,000 years ago. In all there are 365 steps to the pyramid – one for every day of the year.

The pyramid is 24 metres high with a six-metre temple on top dedicated to one of their gods, Feathered Serpent. Every spring, the sun's rays going down the steps of the pyramid create a shadow that resembles a snake descending the steps! Other buildings in the site are a temple (the Temple of the Warriors), a large ball court and an observatory.

1. Which of the Wonders is a.) the oldest b.) the newest?
2. Which of the Wonders impresses you the most? Why?
3. Which of the Wonders are in a.) South America b.) Asia?
4. Choose one of the Wonders and find out as much as you can about it. Report back to the class with your findings.
5. Make up a list of Wonders of Nature, for example the Grand Canyon, the Giant's Causeway etc. Find out as much as you can about any one of them.
6. Look at the map below and locate each New Wonder of the World.

HOLES

Louis Sachar

Stanley Yelnats lives in Texas. His family has a history of bad luck, so he isn't too surprised when a miscarriage of justice sends him to a boys' juvenile detention centre called Camp Green Lake.

Chapter three

Stanley Yelnats was the only passenger on the bus, not counting the driver or the guard. The guard sat next to the driver with his seat turned around facing Stanley. A rifle lay across his lap.

Stanley was sitting about ten rows back, handcuffed to his armrest. His backpack lay on the seat next to him. It contained his toothbrush, toothpaste, and a box of stationery his mother had given him. He'd promised to write to her at least once a week.

He looked out the window, although there wasn't much to see – mostly fields of hay and cotton. He was on a long bus ride to nowhere. The bus wasn't air-conditioned, and the hot, heavy air was almost as stifling as the handcuffs.

Stanley and his parents had tried to pretend that he was just going away to camp for a while, just like rich kids do. When Stanley was younger he used to play with stuffed animals, and pretend the animals were at camp. Camp Fun and Games he called it. Sometimes he'd have them play soccer with a marble. Other times they'd run an obstacle course, or go bungee jumping off a table, tied to broken rubber bands. Now Stanley tried to pretend he was going to Camp Fun and Games. Maybe he'd make some friends, he thought. At least he'd get to swim in the lake.

He didn't have any friends at home. He was overweight and the kids at his middle school often teased him about his size. Even his teachers sometimes made cruel comments without realizing it. On his last day of school, his math teacher, Mrs Bell, taught ratios. As an example, she chose the heaviest kid in the class and the lightest kid in the class, and had them weigh themselves. Stanley weighed three times as much as the other boy. Mrs Bell wrote the ratio on the board, 3:1, unaware of how much embarrassment she had caused both of them.

Stanley was arrested later that day.

He looked at the guard who sat slumped in his seat and wondered if he had fallen asleep. The guard was wearing sunglasses, so Stanley couldn't see his eyes.

Stanley was not a bad kid. He was innocent of the crime for which he was convicted. He'd just been in the wrong place at the wrong time.

It was all because of his no-good-dirty-rotten-pig-stealing-great-great-grandfather!

He smiled. It was a family joke. Whenever anything went wrong, they always blamed Stanley's no-good-dirty-rotten-pig-stealing-great-great-grandfather.

Supposedly, he had a great-great-grandfather who had stolen a pig from a one-legged Gypsy; and she put a curse on him and all his descendants. Stanley and his parents didn't believe in curses, of course, but whenever anything went wrong, it felt good to be able to blame someone.

Things went wrong a lot. They always seemed to be in the wrong place at the wrong time. ⭐

He looked out the window at the vast emptiness. He watched the rise and fall of a telephone wire. In his mind he could hear his father's gruff voice softly singing to him.

'If only, if only,' the woodpecker sighs,
'The bark on the tree was just a little bit softer.'
While the wolf waits below, hungry and lonely,

> ⭐ What are your first impressions of Stanley and his family?

He cries to the moo-oo-oon,
'If only, if only.'

It was a song his father used to sing to him. The melody was sweet and sad, but Stanley's favourite part was when his father would howl the word 'moon'.

The bus hit a small bump and the guard sat up, instantly alert.

Stanley's father was an inventor. To be a successful inventor you need three things: intelligence, perseverance, and just a little bit of luck.

Stanley's father was smart and had a lot of perseverance. Once he started a project he would work on it for years, often going days without sleep. He just never had any luck. Every time an experiment failed, Stanley could hear him cursing his dirty-rotten-pig-stealing-great-grandfather.

Stanley's father was also named Stanley Yelnats. Stanley's father's full name was Stanley Yelnats III. Our Stanley is Stanley Yelnats IV.

Everyone in his family had always liked the fact that 'Stanley Yelnats' was spelled the same frontward and backward. So they kept naming their sons Stanley. Stanley was an only child, as was every other Stanley Yelnats before him.

All of them had something else in common. Despite their awful luck, they always remained hopeful. As Stanley's father liked to say, 'I learn from failure.' ⭐

But perhaps that was part of the curse as well. If Stanley and his father weren't always hopeful, then it wouldn't hurt so much every time their hopes were crushed.

'Not every Stanley Yelnats has been a failure,' Stanley's mother often pointed out, whenever Stanley or his father became so discouraged that they actually started to believe in the curse. The first Stanley Yelnats, Stanley's great-grandfather, had made a fortune in the stock market. 'He couldn't have been too unlucky.'

At such times she neglected to mention the bad luck that befell the first Stanley Yelnats. He lost his entire fortune when he was moving from New York to California. His stagecoach was robbed by the outlaw Kissin' Kate Barlow.

If it weren't for that, Stanley's family would now be living in a mansion on a beach in California. Instead, they were crammed in a tiny apartment that smelled of burning rubber and foot odour.

If only, if only. . .

The apartment smelled the way it did because Stanley's father was trying to invent a way to recycle old sneakers. 'The first person who finds a use for old sneakers,' he said, 'will be a very rich man.'

It was this latest project that led to Stanley's arrest. ⭐

The bus ride became increasingly bumpy because the road was no longer paved.

> ⭐ Review what you know about Stanley and his family.

> ⭐ What could have happened?

Actually, Stanley had been impressed when he first found out that his great-grandfather was robbed by Kissin' Kate Barlow. True, he would have preferred living on the beach in California, but it was still kind of cool to have someone in your family robbed by a famous outlaw.

Kate Barlow didn't actually kiss Stanley's great-grandfather. That would have been really cool, but she only kissed the men she killed. Instead she robbed him and left him stranded in the middle of the desert.

'He was *lucky* to have survived,' Stanley's mother was quick to point out.

The bus was slowing down. The guard grunted as he stretched his arms.

'Welcome to Camp Green Lake,' said the driver.

Stanley looked out the dirty window. He couldn't see a lake.

And hardly anything was green. ⭐

Chapter four

Stanley felt somewhat dazed as the guard unlocked his handcuffs and led him off the bus. He'd been on the bus for over eight hours.

'Be careful,' the bus driver said as Stanley walked down the steps.

⭐ How does the author lighten the mood of this chapter?

Stanley wasn't sure if the bus driver meant for him to be careful going down the steps, or if he was telling him to be careful at Camp Green Lake. 'Thanks for the ride,' he said. His mouth was dry and his throat hurt. He stepped onto the hard, dry dirt. There was a band of sweat around his wrist where the handcuff had been. The land was barren and desolate. He could see a few rundown buildings and some tents. Farther away there was a cabin beneath two tall trees. Those two trees were the only plant life he could see. There weren't even weeds.

The guard led Stanley to a small building. A sign on front said, YOU ARE ENTERING CAMP GREEN LAKE JUVENILE CORRECTIONAL FACILITY. Next to it was another sign which declared that it was a violation of the Texas Penal Code to bring guns, explosives, weapons, drugs, or alcohol onto the premises.

As Stanley read the sign he couldn't help but think, *Well, duh!*

The guard led Stanley into the building, where he felt the welcome relief of air-conditioning.

A man was sitting with his feet up on a desk. He turned his head when Stanley and the guard entered, but otherwise didn't move. Even though he was inside, he wore sunglasses and a cowboy hat. He also held a can of soda, and the sight of it made Stanley even more aware of his own thirst.

He waited while the bus guard gave the man some papers to sign.

'That's a lot of sunflower seeds,' the bus guard said.

Stanley noticed a burlap sack filled with sunflower seeds on the floor next to the desk.

 Predict what the camp guard is going to be like.

178

'I quit smoking last month,' said the man in the cowboy hat. He had a tattoo of a rattlesnake on his arm, and as he signed his name, the snake's rattle seemed to wiggle. 'I used to smoke a pack a day. Now I eat a sack of these every week.'

The guard laughed.

There must have been a small refrigerator behind his desk, because the man in the cowboy hat produced two more cans of soda. For a second Stanley hoped that one might be for him, but the man gave one to the guard and said the other was for the driver. ⭐

'Nine hours here, and now nine hours back,' the guard grumbled. 'What a day!'

Stanley thought about the long, miserable bus ride and felt a little sorry for the guard and the bus driver.

The man in the cowboy hat spit sunflower seed shells into a wastepaper basket. Then he walked around the desk to Stanley. 'My name is Mr Sir,' he said. 'Whenever you speak to me you must call me by my name, is that clear?'

Stanley hesitated. 'Uh, yes, Mr Sir,' he said, though he couldn't imagine that was really the man's name.

'You're not in the Girl Scouts anymore,' Mr Sir said.

Stanley had to remove his clothes in front of Mr Sir, who made sure he wasn't hiding anything. He was then given two sets of clothes and a towel. Each set consisted of a long-sleeve orange jumpsuit, an orange T-shirt, and yellow socks. Stanley wasn't sure if the socks had been yellow originally.

He was also given white sneakers, an orange cap, and a canteen made of heavy plastic, which unfortunately was empty. The cap had a piece of cloth sewn on the back of it, for neck protection.

Stanley got dressed. The clothes smelled like soap. ⭐

Mr Sir told him he should wear one set to work in and one set for relaxation. Laundry was done every three days. On that day his work clothes would be washed. Then the other set would become his work clothes, and he would get clean clothes to wear while resting.

'You are to dig one hole each day, including Saturdays and Sundays. Each hole must be five feet deep, and five feet across in every direction. Your shovel is your measuring stick. Breakfast is served at 4.30.'

Stanley must have looked surprised, because Mr Sir went on to explain that they started early to avoid the hottest part of the day. 'No one is going to baby-sit you,' he added. 'The longer it takes you to dig, the longer you will be out in the sun. If you dig up anything interesting, you are to report it to me or any other counselor. When you

⭐ What does this tell us about Stanley?

⭐ How did Stanley feel at this moment, do you think?

179

finish, the rest of the day is yours.'

Stanley nodded to show he understood.

'This isn't a Girl Scout camp,' said Mr Sir.

He checked Stanley's backpack and allowed him to keep it. Then he led Stanley outside into the blazing heat.

'Take a good look around you,' Mr Sir said. 'What do you see?' Stanley looked out across the vast wasteland. The air seemed thick with heat and dirt. 'Not much,' he said, then hastily added, 'Mr Sir.'

Mr Sir laughed. 'You see any guard towers?'

'No.'

'How about an electric fence?'

'No, Mr Sir.'

'There's no fence at all, is there?'

'No, Mr Sir.'

'You want to run away?' Mr Sir asked him.

Why does Mr. Sir repeat the phrase 'Girl Scout camp'?

Stanley looked back at him, unsure what he meant.
'If you want to run away, go ahead, start running. I'm not going to stop you.'
Stanley didn't know what kind of game Mr Sir was playing.
'I see you're looking at my gun. Don't worry. I'm not going to shoot you.' He tapped his holster.
'This is for yellow-spotted lizards. I wouldn't waste a bullet on you.'
'I'm not going to run away,' Stanley said.
'Good thinking,' said Mr Sir. 'Nobody runs away from here. We don't need a fence. Know why? Because we've got the only water for a hundred miles. You want to run away? You'll be buzzard food in three days.'
Stanley could see some kids dressed in orange and carrying shovels dragging themselves toward the tents.
'You thirsty?' asked Mr Sir.
'Yes, Mr Sir,' Stanley said gratefully.
'Well, you better get used to it. You're going to be thirsty for the next eighteen months.' ✩

How would you describe Mr Sir's character?

1. According to Stanley's father, what three things do you need to be a successful inventor?
2. Describe the clothes Stanley was given.

3. Describe the people and atmosphere on the bus.
4. Find words and phrases that tell us about the heat and climate.
5. Describe the scene when the bus arrived at Camp Green Lake.

6. The story almost makes the reader thirsty! How does the author convey this?
7. Why would it not be wise for Stanley to run away?
8. Why do you think the boys were asked to dig holes every day? What might they find?
9. What problems might Stanley face in the detention centre?
10. What do you think Stanley will write to his mother?

11. What kind of problems would you face while digging a five-foot hole?
12. Are detention centres/prisons a good idea? Give two reasons for and against.